NAPOLEON
Wrote Fiction

NAPOLEON
Wrote Fiction

Edited, introduced and translated by
Christopher Frayling

ST. MARTIN'S PRESS NEW YORK

The photographs in this book
are by courtesy of the Radio Times Hulton
Picture Library, and the reproduction of part
of the manuscript of Clisson and Eugénie
on the back cover is by courtesy
of Nigel Samuel Esq.

AFFILIATED PUBLISHERS: Macmillan & Company, Limited, London –
also at Bombay, Calcutta, Madras and Melbourne – The Macmillan
Company of Canada, Limited, Toronto.

Designed and printed in Great Britain at
The Compton Press

Contents

List of Illustrations

For my Parents, and for Anne

Preface

IN EXILE on St. Helena, Emperor Napoleon I reminisced about the creative writings of his youth, and in particular about the *Discourse on Happiness* which he had presented to the Academy of Lyon in August 1791:

> At the age of twenty, I sent various writings to the Academy of Lyon, but I subsequently withdrew them. When I read these writings, I found their author deserved to be whipped. What ridiculous things I said, and how annoyed I would be if they were preserved!

Napoleon did not in fact withdraw from the Lyon Essay competition, for the simple reason that the prize offered was worth rather more than his total annual pay at the time, including allowances. He also seems to have aspired to be accepted in Parisian literary circles, and his knowledge of Rousseau had taught him that success in the world of provincial academies provided an impressive start for an ambitious young philosophe.

But it is easy to see why Napoleon later wanted to disown the candid pages of his *Intimate Journal*, the romantic short stories and the idealistic commentaries on current political ideas which are synthesised in the first two parts of the *Discourse on Happiness*. For these writings provide a uniquely personal view of this impressionable young Corsican as he tried to come to terms with an alien system of values. On his first garrison duties in Auxonne and Valence, and during his extended periods of leave in Ajaccio and Bastia, Napoleon had no reason to concern himself with posterity, to adapt his persona to the exigencies of public relations; he seems to have felt the need to commit his morbid and extravagant "rêveries" to paper. "I am not yet eighteen years old", he wrote from Valence, "and I am already a writer".

His writings in the period 1786-93 show how the distinctively Napoleonic elements in his Army Bulletins, Proclamations and

Letters gradually evolved. At first, his style is hesitant and sus-
piciously uneven; he is very prone to the influence of those writers
who are uppermost in his mind at a given time, and his own
works have the stilted quality of exercises in written French.
Later, Napoleon develops two distinct styles; one for the artillery
memoranda, reports and surveys undertaken in French training
establishments, the other for impassioned and visionary laments
on the demise of the Corsican Liberation movement. It is only
when Napoleon has made his final decision to pursue a military
career in France that he takes on some consistent identity as a
writer. In short, as well as providing data for the psychological
biographer, the fictional works of Napoleon reveal the author's
desire to shed the mask he felt obliged to adopt in the day-time,
when he was going through the motions of enjoying his initiation
into French 'moeurs' and society. The 'mask' is a recurring
image in these writings, and it may be that Napoleon was aware
of the significance of 'Veil' and 'Mask' imagery in Rousseau's cult
of transparency : certainly he had read *La Nouvelle Héloïse* many
times, and told Roederer "Je l'ai lue à neuf ans. Il m'a tourné la
tête".

Most of these early writings have been preserved, and recent
manuscript discoveries have provided the raw materials for recon-
structing a large proportion of Napoleon's fictional works. The
only major work for which there is some evidence, but which has
never been located, is a play which Napoleon is supposed to
have written in 1793 : this was a short tragedy, set in Italy. The
history of the manuscripts of Napoleon's early creative works is
worth a separate study in itself. To take one example, the
manuscript of *Clisson and Eugénie* was entrusted to Napoleon's
uncle, Cardinal Fesch, in 1815. Shortly after the Emperor's
death, Dr. Antommarchi obtained the manuscript from Fesch.
In 1822 he sold some sections of the work to Count Dzialynski,
a Polish collector of documents relating to the Napoleonic legend.
Eventually, the beginning and the end of *Clisson* (a total of
thirteen manuscript pages) became the property of the Polish
State, and are currently in the Warsaw library. Four pages of
Clisson and Eugénie, which had at some stage been detached
from the Warsaw manuscript, were until 1955 in the Coppet
collection in New York. The fragments were exhibited in Paris,

and sold at Sotheby's in 1955 to Howard Samuel. They are currently in Coutt's Bank in the Strand. To complicate matters further, the pages of the Warsaw manuscript are numbered continuously from one to thirteen (ostensibly in Napoleon's hand); the pages on either side of the four-page middle section are numbered six and seven. This would indicate that Napoleon himself detached what is now the Samuel m.s. from the main body of the work, with the intention of discarding it. Perhaps he had lost interest in the 'domestic' section of the story, and wanted the final version to run continuously from the first meeting of Clisson and Eugénie, to the subsequent crisis in their marriage. The Warsaw manuscript was first published in French in the newspaper *L'Illustration* in January 1920. The version contained in this volume is the first complete text ever to be published.

The complicated history of these manuscripts has made them difficult to trace. So it is perhaps not surprising that out of an estimated 100,000 books which deal with Napoleon and his times, not one has been a fully comprehensive collection of Napoleon's fictional works. What is surprising, is the low quality of the available translations of these writings. Somerset de Chair's version of *Supper in Beaucaire* is readable, but loose and wordy; the Herold anthology is not really concerned with Napoleon's fiction; the Howard translation of the *Letters and Documents* contains a version of *A Meeting at the Palais Royal,* but this includes at least one dubious reading and omits the last two lines, presumably because they were ungrammatically expressed by Napoleon; Vincent Cronin's recent biography also contains a version of the *Meeting,* but the last few lines are translated in a way which is far too kind to Napoleon; Mr. Cronin's translations of certain passages from *Clisson and Eugénie* are curiously up-dated. There are no acceptable translations which attempt to show the evolution of Napoleon's style.

Any translator of Napoleon's early writings faces a variety of difficulties. The flavour of Napoleon's youthful style, which is compounded of bad French, unfinished sentences and crude Italianisms is difficult to capture in English. Many of his more successful attempts at stylistic elegance were derived from Rousseau, Raynal, Diderot and Condillac. I like to think that any wooden-ness in these translations is a direct reflection of Napoleon's style, not of the translator's.

Perhaps some readers will be apprehensive about the choice of the word 'fiction', as a collective description of the contents of a volume which contains extracts from Napoleon's *Intimate Journal,* and his political essays. It could also be argued that the later autobiographical writings (parts of which are pure fiction) also qualify for inclusion. The selections have been chosen because they all throw light on some aspect of Napoleon's creative technique between 1786 and 1795. The example of the *Discourse on Happiness* has already been mentioned – the Examining Body gave Napoleon a low mark *because* the style was excessively inflated, and betrayed an uncontrolled imagination.

A word about the middle section of *Clisson and Eugénie.* This translation is based on my own transcription of the Samuel m.s., which differs in many significant respects from the only French transcription in existence (the second appendix of Vincent Cronin's *Napoleon*). Any transcription runs the risk of being inaccurate on minor details, for, as Napoleon wrote (and for once he was understating the case), 'the Southern blood in my veins runs as swiftly as the Rhône, so forgive me if you find my scrawling hand difficult to decipher'. Whatever the reasons for the illegibility of Napoleon's handwriting, his abbreviations, omissions, mis-spellings, and grammatical errors make the problems of deciphering immense. The transcription on which my translation is based is as accurate as these difficulties permit; it has been very slightly adapted to blend with the rest of the novel. I have included all the variants and drafts, to give a full picture of the way in which Napoleon achieved his stylistic effects.

The literature on Napoleon is so vast and diverse that I have concentrated the main sources into a (very) select bibliography. Specialists will realise that I have relied heavily on the classic works (Chuquet and Masson) for Napoleon's early life. Despite various post-Freudian attempts to re-write their version of the story, they still remain unchallenged in the field. I have also made full use of F. G. Healey's two books on Napoleon and literature. There are no detailed references and footnotes – the introductions to each group of texts suggest the literary influences which affected Napoleon's style at a given time, and any obscure allusions in the actual texts are elucidated at the beginning of each section. The texts are arranged chronologically; since the dating of *Clisson and Eugénie* is controversial, and since most biographers have assumed that this novel was written in 1795, I have placed my discussion of the dating problems in the final section, although I am by no means convinced that the whole of *Clisson* was written four years after the *Discourse on Happiness*.

I would like to express my thanks to the staffs of the Bibliothèque Nationale and the Palais Bourbon Library in Paris, the British Museum Reading Room and the University Library of Cambridge, for their courtesy and assistance. Also to the librarians of Churchill College who gave me access to Sir Winston Churchill's vast collection of books on Napoleon, and to Mr. Nigel Samuel who permitted me to use his manuscript of the middle section of *Clisson and Eugénie*. There are several other debts of gratitude that I would like to acknowledge here. I thank those friends and colleagues in Churchill College, Cambridge, who helped either directly or indirectly in the preparation of the manuscript of this book, and since it was during my three years' research into Jean-Jacques Rousseau's *La Nouvelle Héloïse* that I first discovered Napoleon's creative writings, I also thank Dr. R. A. Leigh, Professor J. Pocock, Duncan Forbes, Dr. J. R. Pole and Stephen Roskill for their advice and encouragement; a knowledge of Rousseau's novels has been invaluable in assessing the importance of those of his greatest disciple. Needless to say, they are not responsible for any of the opinions expressed in this book. Finally, I am deeply grateful to Anne Kirkness for her perceptive criticisms and helpful suggestions. I have enjoyed writing this book, largely because she contributed to it.

CHRISTOPHER FRAYLING

Exeter and Cambridge,
November 1971.

Prologue

ANTOINE-VINCENT Arnault, in his *Souvenirs d'un Sexagénaire*, tells the story of the passage to Egypt aboard the *Orient*, in 1798. The crossing is long, and there are extensive periods of inactivity. After showing the strained relations which existed between the professional soldiers, and the poets, musicians and writers that Napoleon had decided to take with him – "We need poets" he had said – Arnault recounts this anecdote about leisure activities on board :

Boredom was the greatest evil that most of the passengers had to guard against. For the first few days, they had had recourse to gambling. But as . . . the resources of the gamblers were not inexhaustible, everyone's money soon found itself in a few pockets, never to come out again. Then, they had to fall back on reading, and the library became extremely useful. I had the key to it : I became an important man. When he gave me the key, the day after we embarked, the General (Bonaparte) had also given me my instructions.

"Only lend them novels; keep the history books for us".

For the first days, I had few demands to satisfy. I have said why; but when the unsuccessful gamblers took it into their heads to seek consolation in philosophy, I had a little more to do. Our collection of novels was scarcely sufficient.

From time to time, the General came out of his apartment, and walked around the ship . . . During one of his tours, he had the idea of finding out what each person was reading.

"What have you got there, Bessières?"
"A novel."
"And you, Eugène?"
"A novel."
"And you, Bourrienne?"
"A novel."

M. de Bourrienne was holding a copy of *Paul et Virginie*, a work which, incidentally, he detested. Duroc was also reading a novel, and so was Berthier, who . . . had asked me for something sentimental, and had fallen asleep over the passions of *Young Werther*.

"Books for lady's maids", said the General, testily (he had been plagued by sea-sickness for a quarter of an hour). "Only give them history books. Men should read nothing else."

Foreword

CLAIRE DE Rémusat, in her *Mémoires,* transcribed a dinner-table conversation she had with Napoleon in 1802. In it, the First Consul spoke of his youth, and of his early attempts at creative writing:

> I was educated, [he said] at a military school, and I showed no aptitude for anything but the exact sciences. Everyone said of me, "That child will never be good at anything but geometry!" I kept aloof from my schoolfellows. I had chosen a little corner of the school grounds, where I would sit and read at my ease; for I have always liked rêverie. When my companions tried to gain possession of this corner, I defended it with all my might. I already knew by instinct that my will was to override that of the others, and that what pleased me had to belong to me. I was not liked at school. It takes time to make one's self liked; and even when I had nothing to do, I always felt vaguely that I had no time to lose.
>
> I entered the service, and soon grew tired of garrison work. I began to read novels, and they interested me deeply. I even tried to write some. This occupation brought out something in my imagination which mingled itself with the positive knowledge I had acquired; and I often let myself dream, in order that I might afterwards measure my dreams by the compass of my reason. I threw myself into an ideal world, and I endeavoured to find out in what precise points it differed from the actual world in which I lived. I have always liked analysis; and if I were to be seriously in love I should analyse my love bit by bit.
>
> "Why?" and "How?" are questions so useful that they cannot be asked too often. I conquered, rather than studied, history; that is to say, I did not care to retain, and did not retain, anything that could not give me a new idea; I disdained all that was useless, but took possession of certain results that pleased me.

1

Napoleon's hindsight about the writings of his youth is revealing. Apart from being a copy, with variations, of Rousseau's
description of the writing of *La Nouvelle Héloïse* contained in
the *Confessions,* the Consul's recollections betray some of the
reasons he had for attempting to write down his thoughts on
loneliness, and patriotism, when he had the opportunity of
confiding them to his great friend Alexander Des Mazis. Most
of these works were written while Napoleon was on his first
garrison duties in France: he spent his most creative years
in Valence, Douai and Auxonne.

The young Bonaparte* was with the regiment la Fère, stationed
in Valence, from October 30 1785 to September 1786, and at
the Auxonne artillery college from June 1788 to September
1789. He returned to Auxonne in February 1791, and to
Valence from June to August 1791. In between these periods
of garrison duty, he was on leave in Corsica. At Auxonne and
Valence, Napoleon wrote succinct, thorough reports on the
details of artillery strategy and tactics. These were imbued
with the theories of Bourcet – director of the Staff College at
Grenoble and author of *Principles of Mountain Warfare*; of
Guibert – author of *A General Essay on Tactics,* and of Du
Teil – brother of Napoleon's commander at Auxonne and
author of *Uses of the new artillery in open warfare.* In 1788,
Napoleon was commissioned to draft a report on a series of
tests concerning the feasibility of firing explosive shells from
heavy cannon – previously they had only been fired from mortars.
The actual tests took place on the 12th, 13th, 18th and 19th
August 1788. Napoleon – the youngest of the Commission –
wrote his report, and the other signatories praised its clarity of
expression. The memoranda which the young Corsican wrote
in these years are brief, terse and efficient. Above all, they show
an understanding of the new French doctrines of offensive
warfare. Napoleon became more talkative as he gained confidence in his abilities, and spent more time with the other
cadets of the school at Auxonne, than he had at Brienne. He
was praised by the Baron DuTeil for his "wide knowledge,
great intelligence, and, if anything, over enthusiastic" attitude
to his duties.

* The French spelling of Bonaparte is used throughout this volume.

But Napoleon claimed he "soon grew tired of garrison work" : it was during this period that he wrote his most depressed and morbid essays and stories. He even drafted a melodramatic Corsican tale involving primitive guerrilla warfare, which is full of vendettas, violent reprisals, and bloodthirsty slaughters. Napoleon's *Intimate Journal* includes an impassioned discourse on suicide, containing his fears concerning the fate of his home country, and outlining his criticisms of French social life. Other essays seek to find a personal definition for words like "glory", "patriotism", "virtue", and lament the French army's emphasis on "la gloire". Napoleon's attempts at short stories in this period usually concern charismatic political figures who make immense sacrifices for their ideals – Algernon Sydney, the Earl of Essex, Hakem the prophet; or who swear vengeance on their oppressors – the old Corsican, Napoleon himself in the *Journal*. (For the most recent analysis of these two sides of Napoleon's personality see H. T. Parker's article in *French Historical Studies, 1971.*)

Napoleon later acknowledged his debt to "the positive knowledge I had acquired"; certainly he was impressionable to the styles of other writers such as Rousseau and Raynal. The curricula at Brienne and Paris had had a certain impact on his receptive imagination. When preparing his stories about the Earl of Essex and the Prophet Hakem, Napoleon "conquered, rather than studied history". He took concise and well-organised notes on John Barrow's *History of England* and Marigny's *History of the Arab Peoples* : he then re-wrote certain incidents which seemed colourful, or macabre enough to stand a semi-fictionalised treatment. Barrow is mainly used as a basis for the fast-moving introductory sections which introduce the historical background to *The Earl of Essex*. Marigny is simply used for the outline of the story, which Napoleon re-thinks in terms of a political confrontation.

As Consul, Napoleon reminisced about his inclination to rêverie : but he gave no suggestion as to *why* he should have chosen to write full-blooded, romantic stories, in order to make his unhappy leisure hours in Auxonne and Valence more bearable.

1

Early Influences on Napoleon's Attitude to Literature

In his *Memoirs,* written on St. Helena, Napoleon begins his first chapter with a survey of the history and achievements of the Tuscan branch of the Bonaparte family. In the middle ages, the Bonapartes had apparently been allied to the Medici and Orsini families. Several of them were writers "at the period of the revival of letters in Italy". Giuseppe Bonaparte published a comedy entitled *The Widow,* and Niccolo Bonaparte, a Roman prelate, wrote a *History of the Siege of Rome.* Napoleon recalls, with pride, the existence of copies of these works in the Royal Library at Paris. "In 1797, men of letters, who miss no coincidence, remarked on the fact that since the age of Charlemagne, Rome had twice been threatened by great foreign armies; at the head of one of which had been the Constable de Bourbon, and at the head of the other, one of the distant descendants of the family of his historian".

Napoleon's father, Charles-Marie Bonaparte, had a local reputation in Corsica for his eloquence, and for his inflammatory "proclamation to the youth of Corsica" which exhorted young Corsicans to die with glory rather than outlive the hope of independence.

Napoleon could remember certain phrases of this proclamation, and cited one in particular on St. Helena : his version is very close to the original. Charles Bonaparte was also fluent in the French language – a rare qualification in early eighteenth-century Corsica. He wrote verses in Italian which were stylish, if not particularly polished. He wrote short essays against religion in the Voltairean manner. In a sonnet to his brother-in-law Paravacini, Charles sang the praises of love "the great monarch", to whom even the noblest hearts bow down in homage, and in another sonnet written for the wedding festivities of Marbeuf, the French Governor of the island, he prophesied that the elderly general would have a son, who would be the image of his father, and would live to pursue a spectacular career.

Napoleon's mother, Letizia Ramolino, had no pretensions to interest in French or Italian literature. She came from the "Sartène" district of Corsica – famous for its bandits, vendettas and blood-thirsty family rivalries. In the final days of the independence movement, she accompanied her husband into hiding in the woods and mountains of the island. Aggressively, she retained her Corsican identity until she died over ten years after her son Napoleon. She never lost her native accent, or her "Corsican gibberish", as Emperor Napoleon later remarked. Her letters are full of coarse phrases, and words from the Corsican patois, which she never attempted to refine.

"Me croyez-vous *houreuse?*" she wrote in 1809. "Je ne le *souis* pas, quoique mère *dou* quatre rois. De tant d'enfants je n'en ai pas *oune* seul auprès de moi. Ce *povero Luigi* est un honnête homme, *ma* il a bien des chagrins, il en a pardessus la *testa. Jouseph* ne m'ecrit *mai* : il ne *pou* avoir pour moi que des attentions, car il m'offrirait des présents que je n'en voudrais pas. Je suis *più* riche que mes enfants. J'ai *oune millione* l'année; je mets plus de la *metà* à l'épargne. *L'emperour* me dit que je *souis* une vilaine, que je ne donne jamais à *mangiare*; je le laisse dire. Il se plaint de ses frères; je *loui* dis : 'Vous avez tort et raison; vous avez raison si vous les *paragone* à vous, vous êtes *oune* merveille, *oun* phénomène, *qualche* chose d'extraordinaire; *ma* vous avez tort si vous les *paragone* aux autres rois, *perchè* ils sont *soupérieurs* à *tutti.'* " (Quoted in Chuquet's *Jeunesse de Napoléon.*)

Napoleon learned to read, in Italian, at a primary school in Ajaccio. At the age of nine, together with his brother Joseph, he started his education in France : Napoleon would not see Corsica again until eight years later. The Abbé Chardon, who taught Napoleon to speak French at the college of Autun in 1779, claimed that his Corsican pupil had learned to translate and to hold conversations in the language within three months. "He could even write short passages". Napoleon would listen attentively to Chardon's explanations, but would lose concentration when the Abbé recapitulated at the end of the lesson. When his French master scolded him, Napoleon would reply "I already know all that". Bourrienne, who was with Napoleon when he went on to the military preparatory school at Brienne in May 1779, tells a different story; apparently the Corsican arrived at Brienne only speaking his native dialect, and needed private tuition in French.   (It is important to remember, however, that Bourrienne is not a completely trustworthy source.)

In many of his early writings (from 1786 to 1791) Napoleon used certain words which seemed to be an amalgam of both French and Italian (for example at the end of the *Dialogue on Love*) or which were simply invented (for example in *The Mask of the Prophet*). Whether it was because he wrote hurriedly – he certainly had no aspirations to publish his literary works – or because his mind worked faster that his pen, which he later claimed, Napoleon frequently used such Italianisms as "regrader", "ultimer", "courtisantes", "immétriguer", and the verb "procurer de", followed by an infinitive.

On his first active duties at Valence and Auxonne he still did not have complete mastery of the French language, and on his first leave to Corsica, Napoleon had to re-learn the Italian language in order to understand the unpublished manuscripts he was studying in Bastia in preparation for his projected *History of Corsica*. On March 28 1789, Napoleon wrote to his uncle the Archdeacon, and asked him in future to write in Italian.   It seems that whatever language he spoke in – French or Italian – he was uncomfortable. On the Italian campaign, various army spokesmen exaggerated Napoleon's Corsican pronunciation to gain a quick laugh. Even on St. Helena, the Emperor could not read aloud in a completely comprehensible way. During the Consulate, he told his mother that he had always found languages difficult to master.

Bourrienne wrote of Napoleon's difficulties, in his *Mémoires*: "Bonaparte was insensible to the charms of poetic harmony. He had not even sufficient ear to feel the rhythm of poetry, and he never could recite a verse without violating the metre; yet the grand ideas of poetry charmed him".

Bourrienne later mentions how General Bonaparte drew up the list of books for his travelling camp library.

The autograph copy of this list contains some of those orthographical blunders which Bonaparte so frequently committed. Whether those blunders are attributable to the limited course of instruction he received at Brienne, to his hasty writing, the rapid flow of his ideas, or the little importance he attached to that indispensable condition of polite education, I know not. Knowing so well, as he did, the authors and generals whose names appear on the list, it is curious he should have written *Duecling* for Duguesclin, and *Ocean* for Ossian. The latter mistake . . . puzzled me not a little.

Arnault recounts how Napoleon read his favourite poem – *Témora* by Ossian – on board the flagship Orient in 1798.

He never did justice to what he was reading. On account of his lack of practice at reading aloud, his tongue frequently became twisted around words. Sometimes he replaced a T by an S, sometimes an S by a T. Often he . . . murdered the words he was reading, or, substituting one word for another (the effect of his haste), he made his enthusiasm seem less *epic* than *burlesque* . . .

According to Méneval's *Mémoires*, Napoleon would often mispronounce the word "infanterie" as "enfanterie", and "afin que" as "enfin que". However, when he really felt the necessity, Napoleon could avoid orthographical and grammatical faults. His first letters to Marie-Louise, before they actually met, contain very few errors : later, Napoleon's letters to her are full of elementary mistakes. Perhaps Napoleon wished to sustain his distinctive act : critics of Napoleon's style – Désiré Nisard and Stendhal among them – claimed that, in Claire de Rémusat's words, "his grammatical irregularities often gave his words an unexpected power".

Some of Napoleon's early essays seem to be exercises in written French, and there is a parallel development in the years 1786 to 1793, between the progress of his career, and his literary style. At first, Napoleon would write romantic, Corsican tales or histories as an antidote to dull French garrison life. He seldom wrote these while actually living in Corsica. As Napoleon had to decide whether to pursue his career with Paoli the Corsican generalissimo in the struggle for Corsican independence, or with the armies of the French Revolution, which might provide some outlet for his ambition and even be of indirect help to Corsica, his writings became a hybrid of inflated Corsican/Italian styles, and French eighteenth-century literary forms. While trying to link his fortunes with those of Paoli (by writing pamphlets, polemical histories and securing promotion to lieutenant-colonel in a Corsican volunteer regiment), Napoleon also ensured that his commission in a French artillery unit would not lapse. After the Bonaparte family had finally severed all connections with Paoli in June 1793, Napoleon's more mature writings, such as *Supper in Beaucaire,* contain Republican catch-phrases, techniques gleaned from the orators of the French Revolution, and more detached views on the Corsican situation.

2

Napoleon's Literary Education

APART FROM his father's possible influence, and his urge to commit to paper his thoughts on the difficulty of adjusting to French mores, Napoleon also seems to have benefited from his education at military academies in Brienne and Paris: although his particular interest was in mathematics, at which he excelled, the lessons of the "Minims" – the strict teaching order at Brienne – did have some influence in shaping his outlook on literature.

Bourrienne – who was at Brienne with the young Corsican – describes Napoleon's first weeks at his preparatory school:

> His natural reserve, his disposition to meditate on the conquest of Corsica, and the impressions he had received in childhood respecting the misfortunes of his country and his family, led him to seek retirement, and rendered his general demeanour somewhat unpleasing. Our equality of age brought us together in the classes of mathematics . . . and literature. His ardent wish to acquire knowledge was remarkable from the very commencement of his studies. When he first came to the college, he spoke only the Corsican dialect, and the Sieur Dupuis, who was Vice-Principal before Father Berton, gave him individual instruction in the French language. In this he made rapid progress, and in a short time he had commenced the first rudiments of Latin. But he evinced such a repugnance for this study that at the age of fifteen he was not out of the fourth class. There I left him very speedily, but I could never beat him in the mathematical class, in which he was undoubtedly the cleverest pupil at the college. I used sometimes to help him with his Latin themes and versions, in return for the help he gave me in the solution of problems, at which he developed a degree of readiness and facility which perfectly astonished me.
>
> When at Brienne, Bonaparte was remarkable for the dark colour of his complexion (which, subsequently, the climate of France somewhat changed), for his piercing and scrutinizing

glance, and for the style of his conversation both with the masters, and his fellow-students. His conversation almost always bore the appearance of ill humour, and he was certainly not very amiable. This I attribute to the misfortunes his family had sustained, and the impressions made on his mind by the conquest of his country.

Towards the end of his life, Napoleon talked to Las Cases on St. Helena about his childhood in Corsica : "He dwelt much on the charms of his native country, which, from his early recollection, was to him superior to any other spot in the world. He thought that the very smell of the earth would enable him to distinguish his native land — even if he were conducted blindfold to her shores".

Napoleon arrived at Brienne at the age of nine : he was the first Corsican to go there under a new scholarship scheme for the sons of impoverished nobility. His father — always a master in the art of opportunism — managed to secure the award in 1778. Charles Bonaparte had deserted the cause of independence after Paoli was sent into exile to England : since then, he had sided with Marbeuf, the French Governor of Corsica — in 1777 he had even gone to Versailles as leader of a commission from the island. It was through Marbeuf that Charles, having established the claim of the Bonaparte family to nobility for over ten generations, succeeded in arranging for his son's education.

Bourrienne gives evidence of Napoleon's bitterness about his father's careerism : "I will never forgive my father (said Bonaparte at Brienne) for having concurred in the union of Corsica with France. He ought to have followed Paoli's fortune, and have fallen with him". By contrast, Napoleon was reported to have claimed on St. Helena that Charles Bonaparte had never deserted Paoli at all, and that he had "no real desire" to act as he subsequently did. Nevertheless, the "misfortunes his family had sustained", which made the young Napoleon so pensive and morose in his early days at Brienne, probably concerned this issue. He must have known that he owed his very position at the school to his father's machinations and consequent promotion into the world of diplomatic relations between Corsica and France.

By the standards of Brienne, Napoleon was not of respectable lineage : he was a small-time provincial noble from a country which the students knew little about, save that it had been conquered by France. On various occasions Napoleon felt impelled to defend his home country in stand-up fights with the other young gentlemen. Even in lesson times, this proud Corsican must have found the attitude of the staff insufferable. His geography masters only mentioned Corsica as a dependency of Italy, and considered that the essential background for studying the island consisted of a long list of political divisions and sub-divisions on the peninsula. This list included Savoy, Genoa, Venice, Parma, Modena, Tuscany, Naples and Sardinia!

When, in June 1782, the son of the Commandant at Bastia was admitted to Brienne, some students presented him to Napoleon, by way of a joke, as a native of Genoa. The very mention of the word made Napoleon completely lose control : he shouted (in Italian) "are you really of that cursed nation?" and proceeded to grab the new arrival by the hair. It took two weeks for Napoleon to be persuaded that his fellow-student really came from Bastia. The teaching staff provoked him at the dinner-table by "designedly making some remarks disrespectful of Paoli, of whom they knew the young Corsican was an enthusiastic admirer". Napoleon pronounced his first name "Napollione" : the other students soon changed this to "la paille au nez".

By nature a sombre, reflective child, Bonaparte seems to have responded to this uneasy social situation by working immensely hard. He organised his time economically and efficiently, developed a strong desire to finish any work he had in progress, and evolved a technique for clarifying and assimilating his reading. The pupils at Brienne were each given a little allocation of ground in the garden of the school to cultivate in their leisure hours : Napoleon persuaded two of the students to give him their little portion of land. He then built a "Hermitage", where he would sit in the foliage, alone, and read while the others were engaged in sports. When he later spoke to Roederer about these years, Napoleon claimed that he first read *La Nouvelle Héloïse*, in French, at the age of nine, and that "Il m'a tourné la tête". This is doubtful, but Bourrienne was constantly amazed by his friend's conscientiousness – provided the subject matter of his reading seemed to have some utility. Latin, German, and French grammar, apparently, did not.

"Generally speaking, Bonaparte was not much liked by his comrades at Brienne. He was not sociable and rarely took part in their amusements."

But Napoleon could not return home : it was a basic rule at Brienne that, except in emergencies, no boy was ever to leave the school to visit his parents, during the five to six years course. While Napoleon was cloistered in the monastic seclusion of Brienne, two of his sisters were born – Pauline in 1780 and Caroline in 1782 – and he only saw his father once in this period. Napoleon did, however, write to ask for books on Corsica, such as Boswell's account of the island.

The basis of the curriculum taught at Brienne was contained in a directive issued by Saint-Germain, the French Minister of War. In theory the students were to be taught German instead of logic, Latin in order to read the great histories, and as little verse composition and rhetoric as possible. The main subjects were to be history, geography, French drama, mathematics and drawing (particularly plans of fortifications and quick sketches of landscapes). The small Catholic teaching order at Brienne, the "Minims" – who were so low in numbers that they had to call in lay teachers for mathematics and modern languages – interpreted the directive to suit their unusual situation.

The literary course commenced in the "septième" ("classe de grammaire") and continued to the "seconde". No Greek was taught. Latin played an important part in the course, and pupils were taught to find analogies between French and Latin poems : they would recite the fables of La Fontaine, then those of Phaedrus. In the "classes supérieures" there was more emphasis on history : the reading list included Cicero's speeches in defence of Milo, Caesar's *Commentaries,* the 1st and 21st books of Livy and selected books from the *Aeneid.*

All the classes were taught "French language"; the "classes supérieures" went on to study "French literature". Advanced pupils were taught the elements and principal features of rhetoric and elocution. Finally, they were expected to understand, and be able to emulate three categories of style. The "simple style"

– with La Bruyère as a model, the "restrained style" – with Fénelon's *Télémaque* as a model, and the "sublime style". The "Minims" emphasised the pitfalls of the latter category which could easily become a "pompous hotchpotch of empty phrases and words".

Different poetic styles were examined, with reference to examples from Homer, Virgil, Tasso, Milton and Voltaire, and approaches to the fable form were analysed with reference to Aesop, La Fontaine, Phaedrus and La Motte. The syllabus also covered pastoral poetry, the ode, the satire, the epigram, the madrigal and the sonnet.

The basic source book for the history course was René Vertot's *History of the Knights of Malta*. The pupils had to learn long passages by heart, and make short précis of the text. In the "classes supérieures", the reigns of Louis XIV and XV were also studied, including the Seven Years War with its "disasters", the "stupendous conquests" of the English, and the beginnings of Louis XVI's reign; Napoleon had to remember the fact that "King Louis came to the throne for the happiness of the French nation".

In his geography lessons, the Corsican student had to learn, and recite, long lists of facts about France: the names of rivers, ports, civil and military governments, local divisions and sub-divisions, archbishoprics and bishoprics, universities and academies, parlements, pays d'états, councils of all varieties and dukedoms. He was also expected to know the names of the counties of England, Scotland, Ireland and Wales, and the equivalent local administrative divisions of Sweden, Russia and Prussia!

Finally, under the direction of two masters, Frédéric and Marzot, there were lessons in French music – both vocal and instrumental. But in 1783, these were replaced by a new language course in English, under a M. Calonne. (For further details on the curricula at Brienne and Paris see Chuquet's *Jeunesse* . . . , Bartel's *Jeunesse inédite* . . . and Healey's summary of Chuquet and Masson in *The Literary Culture of Napoleon.*)

It is difficult to assess the impact of the literary courses at Brienne on the young Napoleon. Lucien Bonaparte later claimed that if the teaching had been more strict, his brother might have learned more about grammar and spelling: "This part of his education was severely neglected; it seems that at the Military School, they did not attach much importance to it, and I have met several of Napoleon's fellow students who were no stronger at it than he was". For whatever reason, Napoleon never learned to write legibly.

Various biographies of the Emperor, written during or after the St. Helena exile, claim that he won prizes and distinctions at Brienne. They insist that when the Duke de Deux-Ponts visited the school, the Corsican scholar was presented as the prize pupil, and was given a gold watch. Napoleon himself later claimed that he won a gold medal worth fifty louis for his *Discourse* written for the Academy of Lyon in 1791. The Deux-Ponts anecdote is apocryphal – and the prize was withheld by the Academy for the year that Napoleon entered the competition.

Napoleon preferred to study French than Latin : in the Public Examinations of 1780 he was examined on the laws governing syntax contained in Wailly's pocket grammar. He questioned the value of writing in a dead language and preferred to read Latin histories in translated versions which interpreted the classical world picture in terms of eighteenth-century mores. One major reason for his dislike of Latin may have been that it was not taught in the Ecole Militaire in Paris; he had set his sights on further education there. When he later founded his Military Schools (the Prytanée) Napoleon distinguished between those who wanted to pursue a military career, and those who intended to lead a civilian life : only the civilians had to learn Latin. Napoleon's main interests seem to have been History and Geography and his main aptitude Mathematics. His attitude to German and Latin studies gives us some idea of the way he treated the formal teaching of the "Minims" – the constant reiteration by heart of selections from French classical theatre, the bread and butter courses on the French political tradition, and the emphasis on syntax and grammar in Latin lessons.

But whatever shortcomings the literary course at Brienne may have had, the "Minims" did give Napoleon his first introduction to seventeenth-century literature and drama : at various stages in his career he was to consider Corneille and Racine as possessors of "powerful understanding, and a vast knowledge of the human heart". On St. Helena, the Emperor said he would have made Corneille a prince, but, adds Bourrienne, "at the time he spoke to me of Corneille, he had no thought of making either princes or kings". The school at Brienne, by its oppressive social situation, forced Napoleon back onto his own resources. In these years, he began his long process of self-education – in the Hermitage or even, it seems, in lesson-time. Reading avidly (usually from history or geography) he would write his own summaries of the works he was studying, classifying them, interpreting their standpoint, and generally "mastering history". He was noted for the amount of books he borrowed from the school library – for example Plutarch's *Lives* and Tasso's *Jerusalem Delivered*. He also read *Les Jardins* by the Abbé Jacques Delille at this time. One episode stuck in his mind; in 1791 he quoted it in the *Discourse* to the Academy of Lyon. The episode concerned Potaveri, the Tahitian, who is taken to Paris from his island home. Potaveri is moved only by the sight of a tree which also grows in Tahiti – it makes him think for a moment that he is back at home.

Napoleon's particular interest in this incident in many ways explains his attitude to the traditional teaching methods of the "Minims" : an extended course in the classics of French culture, studied against the background of French political structures could not have had much appeal.

Yet he does not seem to have sought any personal outlet from the intense pressures of life at Brienne : he received his First Communion there, but never found in religion the consolation he later found in writing. His daily attendance at chapel was part of the routine of school life. In any case, those officiating at daily mass were not renowned for their serious attitude towards the duty. Father Château took four and a half minutes over the service, and Father Berton, the under-principal, took nine to ten minutes. Father Aria, who took 18-20 minutes, was considered boring and self-indulgent.

Nor did Napoleon feel the urge to sublimate his depressions in sexual pleasure : Brienne was infamous in the world of royal military schools for its "indecencies" and for the number of homosexual "nymphs" who studied there – the "Minims" themselves were considered "difficult to shock". But he showed no interest in this, or in any form of sexual activity.

Napoleon left Brienne for the Royal Military College at Paris on October 30th 1784, aged fifteen. The monastic supervision of his first French school was replaced by close military supervision at Paris. The College was famed as the best riding school in Europe; after Brienne, its surroundings and facilities were luxurious. Napoleon wrote his first Discourse at this time – an attack on the comfortable life enjoyed by gentlemen-cadets at his Paris school. Significantly, he emphasised the difficulty of adjusting to one's home background, after such an affluent existence: the students might easily be embarrassed by their own parents.

> The King's pupils – all poor gentle folk – can only leave the school . . . with a love for conceited and vain sentiments, so that when they return to their homes, far from sharing the modest means of their families with pleasure, they will tend, perhaps, to be embarrassed . . . and to disdain such a modest household. Instead of maintaining so many domestic servants . . . who serve these pupils with their meals every day; instead of parading such a costly show of horsemanship . . . would it not be more important, without in any way interrupting their course of studies to compel the students to be self-sufficient, to make them eat army ration bread, to get them used to the idea of brushing and cleaning their own clothes, and shining their own boots and shoes? . . . Since all the students are destined for military service, is this not the only, true education which should be given them? Subjected to a sober way of life, accustomed to being responsible for their own upkeep, they would become more robust, would be able to withstand the inclemencies of the seasons, to support the strains of war with courage, and inspire respect and blind devotion from those soldiers under their command.

NAPOLEON WAS fifteen years old when he wrote this: he dedicated the Discourse to his under-principal at Brienne, Father Berton.

Bonaparte seems to have taken a more active part in the camaraderie which existed among the cadets of the school; in turn, they accepted his right as a Corsican to be there. He made friends more easily, and had one close friend in Alexander Des Mazis. There were some social difficulties, however : the gentlemen-cadets of high birth (a prince de Rohan, cousin to the King, a duc de Fleury, a Laval-Montmorency) all of whom paid their own fees, tended to despise the assisted students. Napoleon later boasted of the number of bloody noses he caused fighting over this very issue, and his Discourse may have been a gesture against the haughty fee-payers. The other pupils sometimes complained that Napoleon was over-eager to give them advice, and to take it upon himself to look after their moral welfare : he constantly *looked* as if he disapproved of them.

But the Corsican gentleman-cadet still identified with his home country, and dreamed of its liberation by Paoli – with help from himself. His first attempts at writing verse were on this subject : he wrote a long poem on Corsican liberty – as an exercise in the French language! The work began with the description of a dream. Asleep in a cave, Napoleon sees the spirit of his country. She puts a dagger in his hand and says, "You will be my avenger". He declaimed this part of the poem to his friend Laugier de Bellecour, at the top of his voice, brandishing a rusty knife for extra effect.

Napoleon evidently made his views on Corsica well known. Another cadet, who enjoyed scribbling cartoons of his fellow students over the blank pages of his atlas, drew one of cadet Bonaparte : the young Corsican is striding away to help Paoli's movement. Behind him is the tiny figure of an elderly teacher, who is holding his pupil back by the pigtail on his wig. There is a determined look on Bonaparte's face, as he ignores the schoolmaster and clutches a musket. The anonymous artist added the caption : "Bonaparte rushes to help Paoli, to rescue him from the hand of his enemies". On another occasion, Napoleon was summoned before the school administrators. He was told, "You are one of the King's pupils; you must remember that, and try to moderate your love for Corsica. After all, Corsica is part of France".

One major difference between Paris and Brienne was the

greater emphasis on teaching at the Royal Military School. There were four classes – each of two hours – a day. The same teacher supervised the whole course in any one subject. Latin was not taught, and the only literary study was French. Napoleon's French teacher was Louis Domairon, the author of *General Principles of Literature* (1785).

The basic method of Domairon's book was the standard one : it consisted of a long list of facts and selections, with a short commentary attached to each example. The aim was to give "general, but precise notions" about French literature. The book was based on Domairon's lessons at the Royal Military School. Grammar was to be studied first – then the student was considered ready to appreciate the "beauties of eloquence and poetry". The text-book passes from a theoretical analysis of grammar and syntax to a statement of principles underlying the study of literature for both prose and verse.

The first part of *General Principles* is subdivided into three sections.

1. The art of writing correctly, including an analysis of the "nature of words and their arrangement".
2. The art of writing agreeably, including a "dissertation on style".
3. The art of writing "pathétiquement".

One part of the third section was of particular use to the gentlemen-cadets. It was important that they should be aware of the accepted way of writing letters – the protocol, and the permitted stylistic flourishes – so the cadets were taught the precepts, with examples, of the epistolary style.

Domairon's text-book also includes an essay on the "Rules of Literature", in which he distinguishes the separate stylistic rules which govern the writing of different genres.

In fact, Napoleon remembered Louis Domairon all his life. He sought out his old French master, found him working in Dieppe, and promoted him to the rank of Inspector-General in the Imperial University.

This attitude to Domairon's manual is surprising, because the author/teacher was often criticised by the senior authorities at Paris for placing too much emphasis on literary studies. He was told to remember that the pupils were destined for a military

career, that they did have other lessons to attend, and that if
he insisted on using the *General Principles* as a basis for his
course, he should beware of teaching the pupils unnecessary
branches of the subject. In short, he should reduce his syllabus
to "indispensable notions about literature". The minister Ségur
did not authorise the book for all the royal schools because he
found it too detailed for general use.

Nonetheless, Domairon's course and book made a powerful
impression on the young Napoleon : he learned passages from
Corneille's *Cinna* in the classroom at the Royal Military School
which he could quote twenty years later. Contemporaries of
Napoleon at the school were also impressed by the dramatic
way in which the French master would project his ideas (see
Chuquet op. cit.).

Yet, even though Domairon and the "Minims" had been
preoccupied with *form* and *grammatical precepts* in literature,
Napoleon's writing style does not seem to have been directly
affected by the teaching. Domairon himself was struck by the
extravagance and exaggeration of Napoleon's style. He likened it
to "granite, heated up in a volcano". Napoleon's German
teacher, Baur, refused to allow the Corsican to take part in his
lessons; "He is a complete fool", he said. When told that Napoleon had succeeded in passing his artillery examination, Baur
commented, "Well at least he knows something then".

In 1785, Napoleon passed his final examinations for a commission as second lieutenant in the French Royal Artillery.
Probably because he took only a year of study instead of the
usual two or three, he was placed 42nd out of 58 candidates.

3

The Evolution of Napoleon's Style

MANY OF the features of Napoleon's early creative works, written while he was on his first garrison duties, are explicable in terms of his experience in his family and at school. He had evolved two distinct literary styles: one for use in professional memoranda and reports, and the other for extravagant and self-indulgent laments about the fate of Corsica. He still had not learned to write French fluently – in ensuing years his short stories and essays abound in mis-spellings, invented words and complex sentences which he cannot finish. At school, having to rely so much on his own resources, he had learned to organise his time, and he developed a pronounced urge to finish any work that was in hand. In his early stories, there is a conflict between this urge and his inability to express the conclusion of the work in a manner which pleased him. He tried moral epithets, and neat syntheses, but he could never finish a story successfully. Napoleon had also evolved a technique of self-education which left him especially open to the influence of those writers who fascinated him at a given time – later, these would include Rousseau and Raynal. At Paris, he started to feel the need to express his vivid, often macabre imagination, on paper. Perhaps because he found it difficult to talk to his fellow-students about his personal anxieties, the pages of his *Intimate Journal* are written in a style which is very close to the spoken word. It is almost as if Napoleon is dictating to himself. His taste for solitude had become marked. At Auxonne, Douai and Valence, Napoleon wrote most of his creative works during the only time of day when he was left alone – after the military duties of the day had been completed. On one occasion, when he was staying in lodgings at Lyon, he complained that the landlady insisted on talking to him in the evenings: "they never leave me alone".

Perhaps because of his distaste for the class-room techniques of the "Minims", and for the teaching of grammatical laws of the French language at Paris, Napoleon's early writings are seldom argued on logical, copybook lines. Instead of defining his terms, he constantly describes some fictional incident, containing a series of images which will create an overall emotional impression of what he means. When Napoleon wrote his *Discourse to the Academy of Lyon* in 1791, his original intention was to present an academic dissertation which contained a well-argued case, and showed a firm grasp of the meanings commonly attached to the moralists' terms he employed. He practised his writing style, and worked on various drafts before reaching the final stage. He wrote short essays on the theory and practice of politics. He looked up as many polysyllabic words as he could find, and somehow managed to squeeze most of them into the *Discourse*. But Napoleon's contribution to the competition still remains the product of a romantic imagination. There are direct cross-references to his fictional works of previous years, and the first two parts of the *Discourse* consist almost entirely of anecdotes, rêveries and short stories. He literally *illustrates* his points – with either a colourful description or an image which can strike an immediate emotional chord. The third part of the *Discourse,* where Napoleon is trying to argue his case logically on a pattern which is calculated to impress the Academicians, is incoherent and, occasionally, incomprehensible.

Like Rousseau the Genevan, Napoleon the Corsican was an outsider in French society. Unlike Rousseau, his response to the situation often took the form of a self-indulgent lament on the political plight of his home country, expressed in violent, even disturbed images. His rêveries were seldom *personal* – the pages of his *Intimate Journal* are very rare for the years of maximum creative writing – they were usually *political,* or expressed in terms of *political situations.* Certainly, one of the recurring motifs of his writings was the urge, expressed in highly emphatic terms, to retire to the country, and to start thinking about the words which were used so often in his everyday life, and which could easily be taken for granted – words like "gloire", "honneur", "fortune". In *Clisson and Eugénie,* and in the more rhapsodic sections of the *Discours de Lyon,* Napoleon imagines himself into such a situation – on paper, he is free to choose alternatives.

But his imagination more commonly expresses itself in a sudden urge to pursue a romantic career in diplomacy or the army. In a moment of depression while he was on leave in Corsica Napoleon proposed to travel to Bengal, to enlist in the British service. After the siege of Toulon, when he was struck off the army lists for refusing to go to the Vendée to fight an "inglorious" series of actions, he thought of visiting Turkey to offer his services to the Grand Seigneur. Typically, he immediately saw the practical difficulties, and planned to go there in a less romantic capacity – as chief of the military representatives of France (see Parker op. cit.).

As Napoleon was forced by circumstances to make the decision to pursue a military career in France and abandon all hope of becoming the Saviour of Corsica, so his literary works directly reflect this decision : the imagery changes, the issues become more *personalised* as Napoleon has difficulty in identifying himself with Corsica. His pamphlet *Supper in Beaucaire* contains a bitter attack on Paoli for betraying the French Revolution. As "the soldier from Carteaux' army" in this fictional dinner-table conversation takes each member of the assembled company in hand, explains why they should toe the party line and accept the rulings of the Committee of Public Safety, we can see that the soldier will never allow himself to be unmasked again. His public writings will no longer contain the transpareucy, the immediacy of his personal creative statements. Even on St. Helena, when Napoleon began to draft his autobiography, the mask is not dropped. "I have commenced my memoirs with the siege of Toulon" he writes, "I do not consider my actions before that date as belonging to history".

Baron Gourgaud tells of the writing of these *Mémoires* on St. Helena and of numerous conversations he had with the Emperor on the subject of his early life and upbringing. In September 1817, Napoleon summarised all that had been said :

> I am not a Corsican. I was brought up in France. I am, therefore, a Frenchman, as all my brothers are. I was born in 1769, when Corsica had already been joined to France. Once, at Lyon, the Mayor wished to pay me a compliment. He said to me "It is amazing, sire, that although you are not

a Frenchman, you love France so much and are doing so much for her".

It was [remarked the Emperor] as if he had struck me hard with a club. I immediately turned my back on him.

PART ONE

First Garrison Duties

Valence-sur-Rhône,
October 1785 to November 1787

After leaving the military academy in Paris, Napoleon was posted to the "Régiment de la Fère du Corps Royal d'artillerie", stationed at Valence. He was in the first company of the fifth brigade of the regiment, the "Bombardiers". As a junior lieutenant his pay was ninety-three livres a month. Napoleon took lodgings with a Mademoiselle Bou in Valence, and had at least one "petite affaire" (with Caroline du Colombier) at this time. In September 1786, he returned to Corsica, in order to sort out his mother's financial problems. This leave of absence was subsequently extended, and Napoleon devoted his spare time to relearning the Italian language, and to reading documents on the Corsican liberation movement. On his return to France, Napoleon went to Paris to press the French Controller General for a government grant which had been promised to his family some years before, when Marbeuf was alive. The grant had been intended to encourage agricultural development in Corsica. He spent a month in Paris, staying at the Hotel de Cherbourg, Rue Four Saint-Honoré. During this visit (the first since his schooldays) Napoleon seems to have had some aspirations to be accepted in Parisian literary circles.

Introduction

THIS SECTION of Napoleon's writings dates from 1786-7 when he was on garrison duty as a second lieutenant in the Regiment La Fère. The Fable, and the short discourse on suicide were written at Valence, when Napoleon had left the Royal Military School and was adjusting to the routine of professional army life. *A Meeting at the Palais Royal* was written during a visit to Paris and *A Parallel between love of Glory and love of Country* at the end of November 1787, when Napoleon seems to have had aspirations to be accepted by the world of the Salons – the "intimate societies" mentioned in the *Parallel*.

The moral contained within *The Hare, the Hound and the Huntsman* gives us a clear idea of Napoleon's early views on the life at Valence : "God helps him who helps himself". His self-reliance, and his individual method of assimilating facts about literature and politics in a way that would interest him, made Napoleon seek solitude in his spare time. We have seen how the young Corsican learned about the traditions of the fable form – from classical times to La Fontaine – and how he rebelled against the constant reiteration of political facts and figures. This fable, a gentle parody of La Fontaine, has a central character called Caesar – a dog ! Caesar enjoys inflating his own achievement, and scaring lesser animals half out of their wits : his inevitable downfall, through an accident of fate, is a comment on the emptiness of words, on the importance of decisiveness in a difficult situation.

On St. Helena, Napoleon said that he disapproved of "giving La Fontaine to children, who cannot understand the fables. There is far too much irony in the fable of *The Wolf and the Lamb* for it to be within the grasp of children. In any case, in my opinion this story is wrong in its principle and its moral. It is false that the strongest reason is the best; and if this does occur in fact, then *that* is the evil, the abuse that should be condemned. So the wolf should have gobbled up the lamb and choked to death as a result."

This verdict on La Fontaine has some similarities with Rousseau's famous analysis of *The Fox and the Crow* and its impact on the mind of a child, in Book II of *Emile*. Rousseau summarised this section of his treatise on Education as follows:

> Watch children learning their fables and you will see that when they have a chance of applying them, they almost always use them in exactly the opposite way to that the author intended . . . they are disposed to like the vice by which one takes advantage of another's defects. (In the case of *The Fox and the Crow*), the children laugh at the crow, but they all love the fox.

Perhaps *The Hare, the Hound and the Huntsman* indicates that Napoleon had not read *Emile* at this stage of his life, for he was shortly to be extravagant in his praise of the book.

The pages of the *Journal* are very scarce for this period. The first, written on May 3 1786 in a moment of acute depression, seems to be the immediate result of an unusually strong fit of homesickness. Napoleon is virulent in his attack on French domination in Corsica : there are parallels with Rousseau's letter on Geneva in *La Nouvelle Héloïse* where the Genevan complained (particularly in the first draft) of financial and political dependence on France, with its concomitant system of values. Napoleon seems to have had little social life outside the regiment at this time, and most of his money was spent on rent and books. His passion for Rousseau and Ossian is apparent in the idyllic image of a Corsican golden age.

The second fragment from the *Intimate Journal* concerns a conversation which Napoleon had with a prostitute outside the Palais Royal. He puts a series of questions to the girl, culminating in a request to hear about how she lost her virginity. As Emperor, Napoleon was later noted for his inquisitiveness – often he would ask a question out of pure force of habit, and would not even think about what he was asking. At Valence and Auxonne, he was still pursuing his course of self-education : he had to find things out for himself. He would read until 10 o'clock at night, and start again at 4 o'clock in the morning. Sometimes he visited local villagers and farm labourers to question them on social and political issues – he continued to do this when he returned to Corsica. *A Meeting at the Palais Royal* has a feel of immediacy : the conversation is vivid and realistic, and shows a talent for writing dialogue which was seldom apparent in his more mannered creative works. The girl's tiredness is expressed in off-hand, short answers, Napoleon's inquisitiveness by eager, interested questions. Characteristically, Napoleon found it difficult to open and close his description of the incident. The crude self-analysis of the opening lines, and the semi-incomprehensible final paragraph are both recurring deficiencies in Napoleon's writing style. This page of the *Journal* has some corrections on it, ("exercez" is replaced by "assouvirez") but these are not concerned with elegance of presentation : Napoleon is more interested in achieving a sustained precision in the use of words.

On November 27 1787, Napoleon began to write an Essay on the misfortunes of Corsica. He abandoned the work after the first few lines. The fragment shows Napoleon's difficulty in finishing complex sentences : either his mind was working too fast and he lost interest in matters of style, or he could not fit what he had learned of grammar and syntax into the structure of his thought. Even as late as 1791, when he wrote the *Discours de Lyon,* he often placed verbs in the wrong part of the sentence, or missed them out completely. This introduction, on Corsica, – which promises to abound in that type of oratory which was compounded of clichés and romantic images, at which Napoleon was soon to excel – is taken up again in his philosophical essay of the same month, *A Parallel between love of Glory and love of Country* (see N. Tomiche's *Napoléon Ecrivain*).

This short discourse is addressed to a young woman, in the manner of Diderot and numerous other eighteenth-century philosophes. It contains a variety of examples taken from the annals of Corsica, which illustrate the concept of "love of Country". To demonstrate the more limited "love of Glory", Napoleon mainly uses examples from the classics, or from French military history. The style of the piece is declamatory, rhetorical – possibly inspired by Rousseau, and even by memories of Charles Bonaparte's inflammatory pamphlets in Corsica.

In August 1789, Napoleon wrote to Father Dupuy, to ask

for critical comments on his projected history of Corsica (no longer extant). Dupuy complained that Napoleon's style was "prolix and declamatory", full of bad French and crude attempts to shock the reader by extreme imagery. Napoleon replied that Dupuy wanted to remove "toute la métaphysique". These criticisms could well be applied to *A Parallel between love of Glory and love of Country*. Occasionally the young Napoleon manages to encapsulate his idea in a neat phrase, and concretise it by a striking image (always his substitute for definition), but he is still impressionable to other styles.

The Hare, The Hound and
The Huntsman

Caesar, that famous pointer dog,
Bragged that his deeds were beyond compare,
One day he trapped in his forest lair,
A horrified hare – with fear agog.
"Yield" he cried in a voice of thunder,
Which shook the distant woodland birds,
"I'm Caesar, famed for his fighting words,
Whose name fills all the earth with wonder".
Jacky the Hare at this behest,
Commending his soul to God's great care
Demands to be told how he will fare.
"Your much respected mongrellest,
If I give in, will it be for the best?"
"You will die." "I will die" said the guiltless hare,
"And what if flight I should suggest?"
"Still death" said Caesar, unimpressed.
"In that case will you pardon me,
Your much esteemed majesty,
But if I'm to die whichever I choose,
Then I must flee – I have nothing to lose."
This said, the warren's hero flies,
Blameless – whatever Cato said,
The Huntsman sees a likely prize,
He aims, he fires – but the dog falls dead.
What saw would La Fontaine advise?
"God helps him who helps himself" . . .
I approve of that idea myself.

On Suicide

ALWAYS ALONE in the midst of men I return home to dream, and to surrender to my melancholy in all its variety.

Which way does it face today? Towards death. At the dawn of my life I can still hope to live for a long time. I have been out of my country for six to seven years. What pleasures will I not taste in four months when I see my fellow-countrymen and my family! Should I not conclude, from the tender feelings which the memory of childhood pleasures arouses in me, that my happiness will be complete? So, what fury leads me to desire my own destruction? It is the question "what is there for me to do in this world?" Since I have to die, I might as well kill myself . . .

If I had already lived for more than 60 years, I would respect the prejudice of my contemporaries and would wait patiently for nature to run its course; but since I begin to know misfortunes, and nothing is a pleasure to me, why should I put up with days that are never fortunate?

Men are so far removed from nature! They are cowardly, vile, cringing! What spectacle will I see in my country? My compatriots in fetters: trembling, they kiss the hand which oppresses them!

They are no longer those brave Corsicans whom a hero could endow with his virtues, enemies of oppression, luxury and the baseness of the courts. Proud, full of a noble idea of his own particular importance, a Corsican used to live happily if he had made full use of his day in public affairs. Night would slip by in the tender arms of a beloved wife. Reason, and its enthusiasm, made all the cares of the day fade away. Tenderness and nature made his nights like those of the Gods. But those happy days have vanished, with liberty, like a dream!

Frenchmen, not content with having ravished everything we cherish, you have corrupted our morals as well. The tableau of my country's current state, and my helplessness to do anything about it, is yet another reason to fly this earth where duty obliges me to praise men whom virtue tells me I should hate. When I arrive in my country, what face should I put on things, what should I say? When his country is no more – a good patriot must die. If I had only to destroy one man in order to release my compatriots, I would set out this minute, and I would plunge the sword of vengeance into the tyrant's breast, to avenge my country and her violated laws.

My life is a burden to me, because I taste no pleasures, and everything is painful to me.

It is a burden because the men with whom I live and will probably always live have a way of life as far removed from mine as the brightness of the moon differs from that of the sun. So I cannot pursue the only way of life which could make me put up with life; hence my distaste for everything.

A Meeting at the Palais Royal

I CAME OUT of the Théâtre des Italiens, and was striding along the avenue of the Palais-Royal. My mind was excited by characteristically vigorous sentiments which made me indifferent to the cold. But as my imagination cooled, I became more aware of the bitterly cold weather, and so I moved towards the passage-ways. I had not quite reached those iron gates when my glance fell upon a person of the fair sex. The time of night, her figure, and her extreme youth left no doubt in my mind that she was a prostitute.

I looked more closely at her: she paused, not in the usual brazen manner, but with an air that perfectly suited her distinct attractions. This I found striking. Her timidity encouraged me, and I spoke to her . . . I spoke to her, I, who have always thought myself soiled by a single look, so deeply am I conscious of the unpleasantness of her profession. But her pale complexion, her frail physique and her sweet voice combined to give me courage . . . I said to myself, "Either this is someone who will be useful to me for the observations I want to make, or else she is nothing but a fool."

"You must be cold", I said to her, "how can you bring yourself to wander in the open avenues?"

"Ah, sir, hope keeps me at it. I must finish off my evening's work". The resigned way in which she uttered these words, the indifference of this reply won me over and I continued to walk with her.

"You look as if you have a frail constitution. I am surprised you have the strength for a trade like this."

"Lord, sir, I have to do something."

"That may be so, but is there no trade better suited to your health?"

"No, sir . . . one must live."

I was delighted, for I saw that she was at least answering me, a success which had not crowned all the attempts I had made.

"You must come from somewhere in the North, since you can stand up to the cold so well."

"I come from Nantes, in Brittany."

"I know that part of the country . . . Mademoiselle, would you be so kind as to recount how you lost your virginity."

"An officer took it."

"Do you regret it?"

"Oh yes, I must certainly do" (her voice took on an animation and fluency that I had not noticed before), "I most certainly do. My sister has done well for herself. Why shouldn't I have done?"

"How did you come to Paris?"

"The officer who defiled me, whom I detest, abandoned me. I had to fly from a mother's fury. Another officer appeared, brought me to Paris, abandoned me . . . and a third one, with whom I lived for three years, until very recently, followed him. Although he was French, business took him to London, and he is there at the moment. Let's go to your place."

"But what will we do there?"

"Let's go. We can warm up and you can satisfy your pleasure". I had no intention of becoming over-scrupulous at this stage. I had already tempted her, so that she would not consider running away when pressed by the argument I had prepared for her, and I did not want her to start feigning an honesty that I wished to prove she did not possess . . .

A Parallel Between Love of Glory and Love of Country*

I HAVE BARELY reached the age of the dawn of passion; my heart is still agitated by the revolution which first acquaintance with mankind produces in our ideas, and in spite of this, Mademoiselle, you require me to discuss a question which demands a profound knowledge of the human heart. But obedience to your demands is the only way in which I can prove myself a worthy member of this intimate society. Consider this discussion, then, less as a product of intellect and knowledge, than as the faithful picture of the sentiments which agitate this heart, where perhaps man's perversity has not yet penetrated.

If I had to compare the ages of Sparta and Rome with our modern times, I would say : here reigned love and there love of country. By the completely opposite effects which these passions produced, one could doubtless consider oneself entitled to believe them incompatible. What is certain at least is that a people abandoned to gallantry has lost even that degree of energy necessary to conceive that such a thing as a patriot can exist. That is the point we have reached today. Few people believe in love of country. A flood of writing has appeared to demonstrate to us that this ideal is in fact a chimera.

Sentiments which produced the sublime actions of the great Brutus, are you nothing but a chimera?

(Romans, the leading people of the earth by the simplicity of your virtues, the strength of your spirits and the extent of your natural knowledge, you were all mistaken!

You raised altars to Brutus as to a hero. Well! learn from me that that great man was nothing but a madman led astray

* This passage has been slightly abridged.

by self-esteem, when he plunged the vengeful sword of the law into the hearts of his sons in the middle of your public square. You believed he was moved by that same passion which transported you all! Well! this sublime passion that you have vaunted so much, is nothing but self-esteem, and you have been foolish enough to let yourselves be seduced in this way by an unexampled ferocity. You have seen vanity conquer paternal love.)

This, sirs, is the sensation I feel at first sight of this question which I must study more closely. Love of glory, it is said, has produced this group of actions which posterity has celebrated under a just title, but to which history opposes the results of love of country.

Can the love of esteem or of glory have produced the overwhelming number of actions which posterity has celebrated under the name of love of country? This is what our modern sophists claim. If, however, we start demonstrating its insufficiency, what can the answer be? What can have been the motive of the famous patriots who hold so distinguished a place in the annals of the universe, what are the primitive passions which make up patriotism? Such, Mademoiselle, will be the object of the ideas which I am going to develop under your auspices. May they be worthy of you, happy always to have caused me the pleasure of capturing the attention of this intimate society.

Let us open the annals of Monarchy. Our spirits are fired, no doubt, at the recital of the actions of Philip, Alexander, Charlemagne, Turenne, Condé, Machiavelli and so many other illustrious men, who were guided in their heroic career by the esteem of men; but what sentiment overcomes our spirits, at the though of Leonidas and his three hundred Spartans? They were not going to a fight, they were running to their death, for the destiny which threatened their country; they faced the united forces of the Orient in order to obey; they were the finest supporters of liberty; but you who today chain the heart of men to your chariot, sex whose merit consists in a dazzling exterior, consider here your triumph and blush for what you are no more. It is in your annals that I will find the greatest proof of the insufficiency of glory. What sort of heroines were they who triumphed in Sparta? I see them, at the head of the other citizens, celebrating the good fortune of their country with cries of joy. "O Thermopylae, you contain the tomb of my husband, may you render the same office to my son, if tyrants ever threaten my country". What! can this be nothing but the base love of glory? But is not the love of glory the desire to hear one's name sung by rumour! Had the Spartan women anything like this to look forward to? Plutarch tells us that they showed themselves triumphant in the temples and the public squares, while the mothers and wives of those who had escaped dared not show themselves. Yes, these are things worthy of one's country. You can see that love of glory cannot have been the driving force of the Spartans.

But, if the love of glory has been the principle behind the action of Republicans and Monarchists alike, what is the reason for the astonishing difference in the sentiments which animate us even at their recital; what are the differences between the actions themselves? Aristides, the wisest of Athenians, Themistocles, the most ambitious . . . were both savers and restorers of the country. They were rewarded with ignominious exile. "O ye Gods, may you forget the injustices of my compatriots, as I myself pardon them", said Aristides, casting a final glance on his ungrateful and beloved country. "Say to my son", said Simonides, as he submitted to his ignominious arrest, "that since I am no longer a citizen, I am worth nothing to him any more; Athens will always be his mother and his country".

Themistocles preferred to drink of the fatal cup rather than to see himself at the head of the Oriental troops, in a position to avenge his particular outrage. He could have hoped to subjugate Greece. What glory he would have had in posterity, and what satisfaction for his ambition! But no, he lived in the middle of the plains of Persia, ever missing his country.

"Oh my son! we would perish if we had not perished!" – energetic phrase which should remain forever written in the heart of the true patriot.

Let us compare these traits of heroism with the actions of Robert of Artois, Gaston of Orleans, the great Condé and that crowd of Frenchmen, none of whom hesitated before devastating the countryside which gave them birth. The first were nourished by the precepts of patriotism, the others by love of glory. Dare to say that patriotism is nothing. Has nothing ever produced anything?

Inflamed by the burning fire of patriotism, severe Dion – great Plato's disciple – leaves the prosperous lands of Attica. Farewell, pleasures which once beguiled his philosophy. He sacrifices his peace of mind. A tyrant rules in his country. Fly then, Denys, fly from these shores, formerly the theatre of your cruelty. Dion had already raised the standard of liberty in Syracuse, but the strange effect of jealousy, that horrible monster vomited by hell in its fury, crept into the hearts of the Syracusans. Fools! they dared take up arms against their saviour; they attacked the legions which came to deliver them and which were faithful to that hero who led them.

What, meanwhile, were the sentiments which animated him? "Strangers, who are trying to defend my life", cried Dion, "I beg you not to shed the blood of my compatriots!"

Was it love of glory that dictated this sublime speech to him? What would the great Condé have done? . . . Speak, gentlemen, what do you think Condé would have done in these circumstances? Syracuse! Syracuse, you would never have forgotten his punishment for your ingratitude. Chained to his chariot, you would have served as a perpetual monument to his glory and posterity would no doubt have applauded his bravura! But these are not the sentiments which move a heart animated solely by love of country. While his barbarous fellow-citizens were trying to kill him with the very weapons he had provided for them: "Strangers", cried Dion, "who are defending my life, I beg of you, do not shed the blood of my fellow-citizens."

The protector of liberty was no longer in the city. Already the tyrant's satellites were shedding rivers of blood. Liberty was toppling from its last stronghold.

Dion rejoiced in his triumph, and saw those ungrateful, perjured wretches who had sought his life, kneeling at his feet. But . . . you are weeping; tears have flowed from your Stoic eyes! What! those tigers who thirsted after your blood, as the price of your first defeat, those tigers now draw forth your tears. O patriotism! how powerfully you work on men's hearts! As the sun disperses the thickest mist, so, great Dion, your aspect dispersed the numerous cohorts of the tyrant. With what pleasure you saw that your own blood had been shed! It sealed the liberty of Syracuse for ever. And you maintain that love of glory produced those sublime tears! You maintain that it produced that brief speech, where a sentiment reigns that only Jesus Christ has since renewed! But no! no! Love of immortality is a personal sentiment, which always yields to wounded self-esteem. Turenne, hero of France, yielded to a personal grievance and hurled himself against his country – but, what am I saying, "yielded"? – he gave a new force to the effects of the vengeance of self-esteem. It is a feeling which can be linked with the most contradictory passions! Condé, (at the Dunes) was animated by love of glory, just as at Rocroi and Nordlinguen.

Is it necessary to seek any further for evidence of the insufficiency of love of glory? Let us open the annals of that Island which is too little appreciated for the honour of modern times; a Corsican was condemned to die on the scaffold. The laws of the Republic demanded it. His nephew was bound to him, not only by ties of blood, but also of gratitude and the tenderest friendship. In a fit of passion, he flung himself at the feet of the first magistrate, the great Paoli. "May I be permitted to plead for my uncle? Are laws made to cause us misery? He is doubtless only too guilty, but we are offering 2,000 sequins to buy his life. He will never return to the Island."

"Young man", replied Paoli, "you are a Corsican. If you think it will do honour to your country, I will pronounce this verdict, and grant you his life". The good young man stood up – the convulsions of his face expressed the turmoil of his spirit well enough. "No! No! I will not buy the honour of my country

for 2,000 sequins. My uncle, I would sooner die in your arms."
Whichever way I look at this heroic reply, I can perceive no
taint of glory.

Were I to continue, Mademoiselle, to go through the annals
of this illustrious nation, what deeds performed for love of
country would I not find there? Gaffori, who combined the soul
of a Brutus with the eloquence of a Cicero – you sacrificed your
paternal affection to patriotism. Neither ambition, attachment
to his property, nor even the imprisonment of his sons by the
tyrants could tempt Rivorella . . . Some Amphipolitans, who
had seen his son Brasidas die, broke the news to Argileonis.
"Sparta has no man living to equal him." "Do not say that,
my friends", he replied, "I agree my son was a worthy citizen,
but within Sparta's walls there are still more than seventy who
are more worthy of our city."

It is in these private responses that this sentiment best expresses itself. Each trait, each word of a Spartan reveals a heart
inflamed by the sublimest patriotism. You who claim the title
of good patriots, who aspire to have that sentiment – here is your
baptism. It belongs only to those souls privileged with virtue;
to those men who, by the strength of their faculties, can master
all their passions . . . to walk in the footsteps of a Cincinnatus, a
Fabricius, a Cato, a Thrasybulus; but you, who simply claim
the titles of good citizens, think of Pedaratus. The Bouillons
were refused some vain title, and Turenne, the invincible ram-
part of his country, Turenne, who had been showered with her
favours, well! Turenne reduced the cottages he had so long
defended, to ashes. When Condé was refused certain honours,
his pride was wounded – and Condé unfurled the banner of
revolution. That is what the thirst of ambition produced in
the two greatest men in France. How Pedaratus – simple citizen
of a famous republic – rises at this moment above these illustrious monarchists! He entreated the tribune of the people to
elect him one of the three hundred – the premier body of magistrates in the Republic. He was refused.

"Sparta, my dear country, you contain three hundred citizens who are more honest than I. Gods, witness my joy! Ah! were I the least loved man in the country, I would happily accept my lot, so long as I was still a citizen."

Protagonists of glory, admit yourselves finally confounded. Pay homage to the truth. Did the Spartans all affect these sublime sentiments to bring themselves glory? Was it a feigned sentiment, feigned by an entire town? However little you know the genius of men, you must recognise that such an imposture would not have lasted long. The absurdity, the boredom of affecting a sentiment which one does not possess would soon have caused the people to shake off a useless yoke. . .

PART TWO

Napoleon Educates Himself

Auxonne, in the Saône valley,
September 1788 to August 1789

In September 1788, Napoleon resumed his duties with the Regiment La Fère, which was now stationed in Auxonne. The Regiment was affiliated to the School of Artillery there; Major-General Baron Jean-Pierre DuTeil, an authority on the latest techniques of artillery warfare, was in command of the Auxonne school. Napoleon now moved into barracks, not lodgings, and started an intensive course of self-education in his spare time – this included a variety of subjects: History, Political Theory, Biology, and Geography. He seems to have made more of an effort to mix with the other junior officers, for they asked him to draft a constitution and set of rules for the "Calotte", their club. Surviving manuscript notes, taken by Napoleon at this time, bear witness to his increasing awareness of, and interest in, current affairs. At the end of March 1789, he had his first personal experience of the Revolution. There was a wheat riot in Seurre, a town twenty miles further down the Saône from Auxonne; Bonaparte was second in command of the group of soldiers sent by DuTeil to calm the disturbance. On July 19 1789, five days after the storming of the Bastille, there was another local riot, this time in Auxonne. The mob occupied the parish church and broke into the tax office. The men of the La Fère regiment restored order, but on August 16 (the day after Napoleon's twentieth birthday) they mutinied against their officers and demanded a share of regimental funds. However, a week later officers and men re-united to take the oath of allegiance to the new revolutionary regime.

Introduction

In 1783, when Napoleon was only fourteen years old, he wrote to his father, from Brienne, to ask for a copy of Boswell's travels in Corsica. By 1789, he was seriously thinking in terms of writing his own history of Corsica – but before that, he had to clarify his ideas on political and social theory. On October 23 1788, at Auxonne, he began a dissertation on Royal Authority with the aim of developing his thoughts on the "origin and growth" of the *name* of king. It was no more than five lines long: but one year before the Revolution it shows Napoleon's aversion to the royalist *principle*. "There are very few kings who have not deserved to be dethroned." Revolutionary ideas could be of use to the Corsican Independence movement. In a letter to Paoli, also from Auxonne, he showed how a list of the vexations of the French people, and of the inadequacies of those who were governing France, would not be out of place in a sectional history of the Island.

In the early months of 1789, Napoleon took a copy of the *Digest of the Institutes of Justinian* out of the library at Auxonne: he learned whole passages which he considered would later be useful to him – according to Roederer he could still recite them during the drafting of the Civil Code. Another work which deeply interested him at this time was John Barrow's *History of England*: he took copious notes on it, tried to clarify the text, subdivide it into sections and tables of facts, and omitted anything he thought was digressive. (See Tomiche, op. cit.)

When he was transcribing extracts from Buffon's *Natural History* a few months later, Napoleon revealed the basis of his note-taking technique. He wrote, on the subject of Bernardin de St. Pierre's theory of tides "not having had this work for long enough, I can take no notes from it. His theory of flux and reflux seems to be rather bizarre." He would read the text through once, then copy extracts, résumés or impressions. When

45

an idea is original to Napoleon, he puts it in the margin by way of an explanatory note.   In his selection from Barrow, Napoleon omits the long, moralising parentheses that were Barrow's speciality, and adds a few Voltairean asides. He keeps up the narrative flow : only once does Napoleon expand his concise, economical style in the section concerning Charles II and James II, and that is during the detailed treatment of sea battles. In his notes on the ancients, by contrast, Napoleon neglects descriptions of battles. The paragraphs of his notebook are clearly numbered, and details he does not wish to forget (for example about Edward II and Gaveston) go into the margin opposite the appropriate paragraph.   Sometimes, Napoleon adopts the *style* of the author he is reading (in his notes on Buffon and Rollin), more often he is characteristically terse and succinct. Napoleon certainly did not equate being chronological with being logical, however. Sometimes, he follows a particular theme through his reading of a book, and puts all the facts concerning it in one long paragraph. When trying to summarise Barrow's paragraphs, he occasionally uses an anachronistic phrase as a bridge passage : he talks of "administrative bodies" in ancient Britain, and of "prime ministers" in Charles II's reign.

But Napoleon is constantly trying to detach himself from dependence on stylistic influences : he tries to find the mot juste to express his impression of a passage, even at the risk of altering an author's meaning. If the concise notes which Napoleon took at Auxonne on major writers of political history and theory find their parallel in the artillery memoranda and reports he wrote for DuTeil, the creative writings which Napoleon attempted at the same time reveal his urge to find a style of his own. The opening paragraphs of *The Earl of Essex,* suggested by a section in Barrow's history which particularly interested Napoleon, show the difficulties he encountered, trying to reconcile these divergent stylistic developments. *The Earl of Essex,* written in January 1789, contains two introductions. The first, which tries to establish the political and social background against which the ensuing plot will take place, is complex and muddled; it tries to stick to Barrow's original. The second is a less general introduction and tries to relate the psychology of the heroes to the historical milieu. The main story begins with a clumsy transition paragraph, but from the entry of the phantom onwards, Napoleon settles down to a convincingly melodramatic style. The action is fast-moving, and lively: the imagery is exaggerated, but effective in the context (Napoleon may even have had *The Death of Caesar* in mind). The occasional clichés ("unfurling the banner of independence", "the dagger of vengeance" etc.) do not slow down the well-sustained pace of the narrative. The influence of Rousseau is apparent: the Genevan's interest in Algernon Sydney (for his views on direct and indirect political relationships) is shown by a series of unpublished manuscript notes he took on Sydney's *Discourse on Government*. These were written in preparation for the *Discourse on the Origins of Inequality,* where Sydney is mentioned, and were later used again for the specifically Genevan polemics.

Napoleon retained his interest in ghost stories all his life. Bourrienne recounts this anecdote :

He often talked a great deal, and some times a little too much : but no one could tell a story in a more agreeable and interesting way. His conversation rarely turned on gay or humorous subjects, and never on trivial matters. He was so fond of argument, that in the warmth of discussion it was easy to draw from him secrets which he was most anxious to conceal. Sometimes, in a small circle, he would amuse himself by relating stories of presentiments and apparitions. For this, he always chose the twilight of evening, and he would prepare his hearers for what was coming by some solemn remark. On one occasion of this kind, he said, in a very grave tone of voice, "When death strikes a person whom we love, and who is distant from us, a foreboding almost always denotes the event, and the dying person appears to us at the moment of his death." He then immediately related the following story :—

A gentleman of the court of Louis XIV was in the gallery of Versailles at the time when the King was reading out the bulletin of the battle of Friedlingen, which was won by Villars. Suddenly, the gentleman saw at the far end of the gallery, the ghost of his son, who had served under Villars. He exclaimed, "My son is no more", and, a moment later, the King named him among the dead.

In *The Earl of Essex,* and in Napoleon's next attempt at writing a short story, *The Mask of the Prophet,* the conclusion is weak and muddled. Perhaps Napoleon felt obliged to end on a moral note, however much this jarred with the foregoing narrative. He took Marigny's *History of the Arab Peoples,* and Amelot's *History of Venice* with him, when he went with his regiment to restore order after the riot at Seurre at the end of March 1789. So there is a directly political reason why the Hakem/Mahadi section of Marigny should have struck Napoleon forcibly enough to write a story about it. In *The Mask of the Prophet,* Hakem's threat to the state is described in terms of a mass movement, based on the gospel of liberty and equality. Mahadi is seen as a father to his people, a paternalistic monarch, while Hakem is a rabble-rousing prophet. These two conceptions of power are opposed: Napoleon does not take sides when he sets the scene for the confrontation. *The Mask of the Prophet,* written four months after *The Earl of Essex,* has similar features: it concerns a charismatic "patriot", who challenges established power, and the action once again moves in a rapid, vital way. Some of Napoleon's turns of phrase – during Hakem's oration to his troops, and the consequent description of the credulity of the masses – have surprising power. Napoleon is beginning to perfect his use of the short, economical phrase, and to adapt the styles he assimilated at school to individual characterisation – for example Hakem's dialogue with God. Characteristically, the final phrase of the story, concerning "la fureur de l'illustration", is grammatically incorrect, and original in its use of the word "illustration". (See Tomiche, op. cit.)

A few months later, Napoleon wrote his third short story: *New Corsica.* This desert-island tale – the first part of which is inspired by Defoe, Shakespeare, Bernadin de St. Pierre and Rousseau, the second by Paoli, Charles Bonaparte, the Abbé Raynal and Rousseau again – changes from an adventure story to a political pamphlet half way through. When the Old Corsican begins to recount his life story, the pace changes, the compactness of the opening paragraphs abruptly disappears, and ensuing pages become a polemic in favour of Corsican Independence and against domination by the brutal French. Napoleon may have had the idea of using the second half of the tale unaltered in his *History of Corsica,* for Father Dupuy's criticisms of that document, written in August 1789, show that there were distinct similarities. Dupuy writes "you choose that this work . . . should be written by an old man who is very near to his death . . . a natural measured style agrees with his character . . . but the figures of speech, the great words and the exclamations seem to me to be those of a young man". Napoleon evidently wrote part of his *History* as the biography of an ageing patriot, who narrates his version of the island's troubles. Many of the phrases that Dupuy singles out as uncharacteristic of an old man, are identical to those contained in the second half of *New Corsica.* Perhaps Napoleon discovered, in the process of writing a short story, that he had a useful means of expressing his views on Corsica in highly emotive terms – which he could then fit into his Paolist history. In the *Discourse* written for the Academy of Lyon in 1791, Napoleon will discuss questions of morality entirely in terms of a series of fictional anecdotes – one of these, which involves the island of Monte Cristo is very similar to *New Corsica.*

The first half of *New Corsica* shows how Napoleon has profited from his experiences with the previous two tales; he can now capture the interest of the reader by rapid narrative development, alternating with brief descriptive passages. There are interesting cross-references between both parts of *New Corsica* and Rousseau's *Emile et Sophie ou les Solitaires,* the little known sequel to *Emile* : in this unfinished story the two characters finally meet again, after a series of picaresque adventures, on a desert island. The opening words of *Emile et Sophie,* where Emile writes to his Tutor "J'étois libre, j'étois heureux", find a direct echo in the Old Corsican's speech. "Nous chassâmes nos tyrans" says the old man with similar nostalgia, "nous étions libres, nous étions heureux." Napoleon could have read this work in the editions of 1780 or 1781.

But he was incapable of finishing either part of *New Corsica.* The narrative clumsily runs into the extended monologue : the impersonal, controlled style of the "Englishman" gives way to a series of histrionic outbursts. The monologue itself finishes mid-sentence : perhaps Napoleon was only writing the second part as an exercise in rhetorical style, and was indifferent about the outcome of the tale.

Dissertation on Royal Authority

This work will commence with general ideas on the origin and growth which the word "King" has had in men's minds. Military government goes well with Royal authority. After that, this work will enter into the details of the usurped authority which Kings enjoy, in the twelve kingdoms of Europe.

There are very few kings who have not deserved to be dethroned . . .

Extracts from Napoleon's notes, taken from the *Histoire nouvelle et impartiale d'Angleterre depuis l'invasion de Jules César jusqu'aux préliminaires de la paix de 1763,* translated from John Barrow's original English version in 1771.

... CHARLES II

1660 Monk was rewarded for his talents. He was made Knight of the Garter and was given the Duchy of Albemarle.

Manchester was made Chamberlain, Ashley, Holles were made Barons, etc. etc.

Sir Francis Hyde, Earl of Clarendon, was made Prime Minister and Great Chancellor.

Lambert and Vane were omitted from the Act of Amnesty.

Cromwell's possessions were confiscated. Harrison, Scot, Scroop, Carew, Jones, Clement, Coke, Axtel and Hacker were condemned. They embraced their fate with the courage and constancy of martyrs.

1663 The King married Catherine, the Portuguese Infanta, who brought him a dowry of 300,000 pounds sterling, plus the fortresses of Tangier and Bombay. He sold Dunkirk for the sum of 400,000 pounds sterling.

1664 Henry Vane, an innocent victim, was executed. A drum was beaten to prevent his oration being heard.

1665 The Duke of York seized 130 Dutch merchant ships, although the war had not yet begun. War was declared on the Republic. The well-known Jean Witt was at that time the Pensionary. Opdam and van Tromp, son of

Martin van Tromp, were in command of the fleet.
The Duke of York and Prince Rupert commanded the
English army. They met near Colchester. The English
had 140 ships and the Dutch 120. Opdam's ship was
blown to pieces. The Dutch lost 90 ships and 6,000 men.

1666   Prince Rupert and Monk attacked the Dutch fleet commanded by Ruyter and van Tromp. It contained 76 ships.
A French squadron came to the help of the Dutch, and
forced the English to withdraw. The English fleet, containing more than 100 ships, was attacked by the combined fleets which numbered only 88. The battle took
place at the mouth of the Thames. The English were
victorious. A terrible fire burned 13,200 houses, 89
churches. The ruins covered 436 acres of land. It lasted
3 days.

1667   The treaty of Breda displeased the whole nation.

1667   Chancellor Clarendon, too serious-minded to be respected
at the licentious court of Charles, accused by parliament,
fled to France where he wrote his history of the great
rebellion. The London Stock Exchange was founded
during this year.

1669   The King asked for subsidies, but Parliament's only
retort was to examine the public accounts. The King
allowed himself to be governed by Clifford, Buckingham,
Ashley : men of the Cabal. He proceeded to make himself
independent. Navy expenses rose to 500,000 pounds
sterling.

1671   Lord Lucas yet again attacked the administration in
front of the King. He said the people were more down-
trodden than if a victorious enemy was crushing them.
The infamous Blood had served in Cromwell's army. He
had assassinated the Duke of Ormond and plotted to
steal the Crown Jewels. By his adroitness, he obtained a
pardon and became the King's confidant.

1672   France, England, the Elector of Cologne and the Bishop
of Munster united to attack Holland. Thomas Clifford

was made treasurer. It was he who thought up the idea of suspending payments from the Exchequer and of re-channelling the funds to pay for the King's pleasures : this destroyed credit.

The Earl of Sandwich preferred blowing up his own ship to the shame of surrendering it.

The two fleets of France and England attacked the Dutch fleet. The battle was indecisive. However, the Dutch appeared to have the advantage. The Marshall d'Estrées made no move during the action.

1673   Charles tolerated Papism : this was the first thing about
(fin-   which the Parliament of this year protested. They passed
ished   the famous Test Act.
Sun-   There was a naval action between the English and Dutch.
day   The English were victorious. Louis XIV granted a
Nov-   pension of 100,000 pounds sterling to Charles.
ember   Parliament caused the King much anxiety. The Earl of
30   Danby and the Duke of Lauderdale were impeached by
1788.   the Commons and the Independent Party only just failed
Aux-   to gain a majority.
onne.)   The Court of Equity is that court of the Chancellery in which the severity of the law is moderated.

1675   The Commons granted 300,000 pounds sterling for the construction of 30 ships.

1678   Titus Oates, a well-known informer (together with Bedloe of Newbury), was the agent used to ruin the Roman Catholics. The Commons ordered that every Catholic should be made to take the Test oath. The Duke of York, who was a Catholic, begged with tears in his eyes that an exception be made in his case. He obtained it by a majority of only two votes. The Earl of Shaftesbury controlled the major faction in parliament. He was leader of the opposition.

Sir William Temple, a renowned diplomatist, was famed for his integrity.

1679   The Bill which declares the Duke of York to be unable to come to the throne dates from this year.

It was discovered that 18 members of the Commons were in the pay of the Court.

The Habeus Corpus bill was passed as an *act*.

Charles dissolves Parliament.

1680 The Opposition party compared the supporters of the
Whig Court to Irish bandits and called them Tories. The Court
and   Party in turn called the members of the Opposition
Tory Whigs, a term of abuse originally used to describe those rigid Presbyterians who lived entirely on a type of milk called whig. These had the Earl of Shaftesbury as their leader.

Lord Russell, a rigid republican, proposed the drafting of a bill to exclude the Duke of York from the crown.

Sir William Jones, Sir Francis Winnington, Sir Henry Capel, Sir William Pulteney, Colonel Legge, Hampden and Montague supported the motion. They held that parliament had the right to change any part of the constitution they wished.

The Bill passed the House of Commons, but was rejected by the Peers, on account of an eloquent speech by Halifax. The Commons complained bitterly about the King. They remarked that with a total of more than one million pounds sterling which had been granted for the navy, he had not ordered the construction of a single ship, that two million granted to uphold the triple alliance had been used to destroy it. The Commons gave the impression that the King himself had joined a conspiracy against the established religion. (A conspiracy against the established religion was thought to have been discovered.) Much blood was shed, including that of Lord Stafford.

1681 Parliament worked with all its might to secure the passage of the Bill of Exclusion. The Opposition had a decisive majority, the King dissolved Parliament and convoked another at Oxford. The members of this new parliament appeared there armed, as if a break was certain. The leaders of the Opposition had already drawn up several bills against the King when he dissolved it.

The Grand Jury is a tribunal composed of 24 members – gentlemen or commoners – chosen without discrimination from the whole county, by the Sheriff : their task is to consider the bills of impeachment presented to the Court. The Earl of Shaftesbury was arrested and the bill of impeachment presented to the jury was rejected, to the great satisfaction of the people.

1683   Charles was triumphant. His cruel and arbitrary administration gave birth to many conspiracies. The Duke of Monmouth, the Earl of Essex, Lords Russell, Howard, Algernon Sydney and John Hampden were the ringleaders and there were several other subordinates, such as colonels Rumsey and Walcot, etc. etc. This conspiracy was called the Rye House Plot. They were found out. Lord Russell, the English Brutus, was adored by everyone : Lord Cavendish suggested a plan of escape to him, but he refused. He died with the composure of heroism and virtue.

Lord Sydney, in whom the patriotism of the ancient Republicans seemed to live again, died in the same manner. Lord Sydney had written a work which dealt with the nature of the original contract on which all government is based. This discourse was found among his papers. The Earl of Essex was found dead in the Tower. His throat had been cut with a razor: the King had been there that morning with his brother. Some children had seen a blood-stained razor thrown out of the windows. Baillie of Jerviswood, renowned for his talents and his integrity, was in charge of the negotiation between Argyll and the Duke of Monmouth. He was arrested and died with a steadfastness worthy of an ancient Roman.

1684   Charles acquired all the charters which incorporate the communities and corporations of the kingdom and intended, so it is said, to sell them – when he died at the age of 54.

1685 On Charles' death, two papers were found written in his hand, which defended the Roman Catholic religion. Charles managed to sustain his authority by following his own inclinations. He was casual, lavish in his spending, addicted to the pleasures of the senses, and a libertine.

JAMES II

1685 The King called the council together, and declared that he wished to maintain the established religion.

On the 23 April he was crowned; but it was noticed that the crown was too big for his head. The communities and corporations of England, deprived of their charters, found themselves to be at the mercy of the King.

Ayloffe, who was related to the old Earl of Clarendon, was arrested with the Duke of Argyll, and accused of being implicated in the Rye House Plot. James interrogated him in person. "You know it is in my power to pardon you", said the King. "That is true, sire", replied Ayloffe, "but not in your nature . . ."

The Earl of Essex

AN ENGLISH TALE

THE DESPOTIC government of Charles II, combined with the grievances caused by his brother, the Duke of York, who was imbued with Catholic principles and persecuted to excess the Presbyterians and the leaders of the opposition party, bred conspiracies and societies for the preservation of the national constitution on all sides.

The Duke of Monmouth, bastard son to Charles, encouraged a disaffection which he anticipated would place the crown on his head. For four years now, Charles had governed without parliament : he feared the activities of those republicans who had led his father to the scaffold, he feared the severe principles of Lords Sidney, Russell and Essex . . .

The Earl of Essex, Lords Russell and Sidney, moved by their common patriotism, conspired against Charles II and his brother, the Duke of York. For four years, this prince had been governing without parliament and the nation groaned under the despotic yoke of an unlawful administration.

The national constitution and the established religion were in danger; royal authority had devoured everything.

The only salvation for liberty lay in the death of the usurper : it was resolved to put this into effect.

Everything had been prepared. The day had been set, the means agreed on, and the same act would have avenged and saved the oppressed English nation.

However, everything misfired, and the lords who led the conspiracy were arrested and sent to the Tower. The moment this news spread among the public was one of those moments of crisis that alarm and discourage virtuous folk.

The Earl of Essex was well known for his harsh code of morality, his austere way of life and his rigid sense of justice. He could well have said, as Cato did, that never having excused himself in anything, he could never excuse anyone else. Lord Russell was the idol of the people : they worshipped him. His gentle eloquence, his virtue, the impartiality which ruled his actions had all enhanced a reputation that steadfastness in resisting royal authority alone had made dear to all good Englishmen. People said of him : if justice came down on earth, she would behave like Lord Russell.

Sidney was one of those unyielding patriots who are guided by the principles of a Brutus, or a Thrasias. He was one of the first to unfurl the banner of independence in Charles I's reign. He alone resisted Cromwell. He alone still hoped for the foundation of the republic. Enemy to monarchies, princes, aristocrats, Sidney had, by deep study, delved back to the original contract which is the basis of all Constitutions. These were the three men that the tyrant held in his power. Russell made no attempt to conceal the truth and his trial presented no difficulty. In vain was he urged to make his escape, nothing could persuade him . . . he died as he had lived. Lord Sidney saw his blood shed in a good cause, and only regretted that he left his country exposed to the fury of two tyrants.

Essex still remained. The people, who had shed tears at the death of the two Lords, furiously demanded the Earl's pardon. The judges, horrified by so many crimes, dared not condemn him. In vain the King commanded them, the Duke beseeched them : they shuddered at the very thought of it, and recognising the abyss which yawned beneath their feet, resolved to save the Earl.

Who could depict the frantic rage which then overcame the Duke of York? He could see his prey escaping from him. The blood of Sidney and of Russell did not suffice to satisfy his rage, and, unable to destroy a nation he hated, he wished at least to avenge himself on those the nation worshipped – those who were involved in passing the Bill of Exclusion. Religion, politics, hatred, spite, need for vengeance, all combined in the Duke's mind into a desire for the Earl's death. However, all was to no avail and the Earl was about to be declared innocent when a terrible occurrence helped the Duke out of his difficulty. This anecdote is interesting enough to merit entering into every detail that has been preserved.

On Monday, 13th September, it was extremely cold : a fog, common enough in the London climate, shrouded the city. The Countess of Essex decided to go and see her husband. The carriage collided with another and after several hours delay she arrived. She found her husband occupied with preparations for departure, for his verdict was already known. After spending part of the day together, they arranged to meet on the following day, Tuesday.

It was not yet ten o'clock when the King, accompanied by the Duke of York, made his way to the Tower. This was contrary to their usual practice, for they had not set foot in there for two years. They left at half past eleven.

Meanwhile, the Countess, who loved her husband dearly, was consumed with impatience to see him again, and having spent part of the night ordering the preparation of his quarters, she eventually gave way to sleep. She had not long been asleep when she was awoken with a start by a noise she thought she heard in her room. It was only a dream. However, she woke up again three times, each time troubled by a mournful sound she imagined she could hear, but which ceased at her awakening. Out of all patience, she called her servants, but sleep reclaimed her and the servants did not come. The sound redoubled. The Countess, naturally courageous, got up, drew back the curtains, crossed the darkness of her room, reached the door.

Picture to yourself a woman, troubled by ominous dreams, warned by terrifying noises in the middle of the night, lost in the darkness of her enormous room. She reached the door, she fumbled for the lock. A cold shiver ran through her body – she was touching a sharp dagger. Even the blood which trickled from it could not dismay her.

"Whoever you may be, stand . . . I am the unfortunate wife of the Earl of Essex", she cried, and far from losing her senses, she stretched out her hand again, found the key and opened the door.

She thought she caught a glimpse of something moving at the far end of the ante-chamber, but she put it down to her frailty, and having shut the door again, went back to bed.

It was eleven o'clock in the morning, and the Countess, restless, pale, and troubled, struggled against a disturbing nightmare.

"Jane Bettsy, Jane Bettsy, dear Jane."

She looked up, for this sound had awoken her; she saw . . . O God! . . . She saw a phantom which moved towards her bed, drew aside the four bed-curtains, took her by the hand, and said to her,

"Jane, you have forgotten me, you sleep, but touch me."

The phantom guided her hand to his neck. O horror! The fingers of the Countess sank into gaping wounds, her fingers dripped with blood. She cried out, hid her face, but looking up again could see nothing. Terrified, trembling, aghast, cut to the very quick by these terrible forebodings, the Countess got into a carriage, and arrived at the Tower. As she passed through Pall Mall, she heard someone in the crowd saying : "The Earl of Essex is dead."

At last, she arrived, the door was opened – O horrible spectacle! She saw the Earl stretched out on the ground, lying in a pool of his own blood. Three great slashes of a razor had killed the Earl. His hand was on his heart. His eyes, raised to heaven, seemed to solicit the eternal vengeance.

Do you think that, dumbfounded, overcome, Jane was about to dishonour the memory of the most esteemed of men by base tears? No. She had the body washed, taken outside, and exposed to public view.

The uproar this spectacle excited in London would be difficult to imagine. They wanted, there and then, to subject his cowardly assassins to the same treatment. The populace accused the King and his brother.

Doctor Burnet was empowered to make thorough inquiries to discover the perpetrators of this murder. Two children gave evidence that they had seen someone throw a blood-stained razor out of the window. The servants of the unfortunate Lord said that he had spent the morning calmly, that at eleven o'clock, they had been told to leave by the governor of the Tower. The identity of the murderers was no longer in doubt.

Meanwhile, in her mortal grief, the Countess had her rooms draped in black. She boarded up the windows and spent her days lamenting the hideous fate of her husband. It was not until three years later, when, after the death of the King, the Duke of York was dethroned, that, satisfied by Heaven's vengeance, she re-appeared in society.

An extract from Napoleon's notes on the *Histoire des Arabes sous le gouvernement des Califes* by the Abbe Marigny.

MAHADI THE TWENTY-SECOND CALIPH

He was very different from his father : he was as great, generous and magnanimous as his father had been small-minded, miserly and cowardly.

He forced the Greeks to sue for peace, and to pay him 60,000 gold crowns.

A prophet named Hakem, also called Burkai (which means mask) because he wore a mask made of silver, had such power over his disciples that they believed him when he said that he wore his mask to prevent men from being dazzled by the light which shone from him. He took possession of several areas of the Khorassan and was besieged in one of them. Immediately, he ordered deep ditches to be dug. He had them filled with quicklime. He had a jar filled with spirits. Then he poisoned the wine he had put aside for his disciples; they drank it and all perished. He dragged them to the ditch, and the bodies of these unfortunate wretches were consumed there. Then he set fire to the spirits and leapt into them. His proselytes have always maintained that he ascended into heaven, and that one day he will return.

Mahadi . . . died, adored by the people and by the whole Empire; he was just and great. He was buried beneath a tree.

In the year 164, there was a most incredible phenomenon : the sun, as it rose – without any clouds or any kind of eclipse – covered everything with a fearful darkness until mid-day.

The Mask of the Prophet

AN ARABIAN TALE

IN THE YEAR 160 of the Hegira, Mahadi ruled in Baghdad; this prince was great, generous, enlightened and noble-minded. He saw the Arab Empire prosper in the bosom of peace. Feared and respected by his neighbours, he applied himself to the task of encouraging the sciences; which were making rapid progress when the peace was disturbed by Hakem, who, from the heart of the Korassan, had started to attract disciples from all parts of the Empire.

Hakem was a man of magnificent stature and a fiery, virile eloquence. He called himself the envoy of God. He preached an uncompromising morality which pleased the multitude; the usual theme of his sermons was equality of rank and of fortune. The people flocked to his banner : Hakem had an army.

The Caliph and the nobles recognised the necessity of smothering at birth so dangerous an insurrection, but their troops were defeated more than once and Hakem expanded his movement every day.

However, a cruel illness, result of the hardships of war, disfigured the prophet's face. He was no longer the most handsome of Arabs; those proud and noble features, those large, fiery eyes were disfigured. Hakem became blind. This transformation could well have moderated the enthusiasm of his followers : he conceived the idea of wearing a silver mask.

He appeared in the midst of his disciples. Hakem had lost nothing of his eloquence. His oration had the same impact. He spoke to them and convinced them that he wore the mask only to prevent mankind from being blinded by the dazzling light which shone from his countenance.

He was placing his trust more than ever in the frenzy of the people he had inflamed, when a defeat in battle caused the ruin of his efforts, a reduction in the number of his followers, and a weakening of their faith. He was besieged, his garrison was small. Hakem – you must perish or your enemies will capture you.

He called his disciples together and said to them :

"Faithful followers, you whom God and Mahomet have chosen to restore the Empire and raise up our nation, why does the number of our enemies make you lose heart? Listen : last night while you were all deep in sleep, I bowed down and said unto God : 'My Father you have protected me for so many years. Have I or my people offended you that you abandon us?' A moment later, I heard a voice which said unto me : 'Hakem! only those who have not forsaken you are your true friends and they alone are the Chosen. They will share with you the wealth of your vainglorious enemies. Wait until the new moon, then dig deep trenches. Your enemies will rush headlong into them like flies stupefied by smoke.' "

The trenches were soon ready : one was filled with quicklime. Vats of distilled liquor were placed on the edge. When everything was completed a meal was served out to everyone – they all drank the same wine and they all died, with the same symptoms.

Hakem dragged their bodies to the quick-lime, which consumed them, set fire to the distilled liquor and flung himself into the flames.

The following day, the Caliph's troops were on the point of advancing, but halted when they saw that the gates were open. Cautiously they entered and found only one survivor, a woman who had been Hakem's mistress.

Such was the end of Hakem, named Burkai, whom his disciples still believe ascended into heaven with all his followers. This example is unbelievable.

Just how far can a man be driven in his desire for fame?

New Corsica

I HAD embarked at Livourne, and was bound for Spain when contrary winds forced us to seek shelter at "La Gorgona". "La Gorgona" is a sheer mass of rock, of maybe half a league in circumference. The island provided little shelter for us but, in our present need, it was the only thing we could do, seeing that our vessel was shipping water in various places.

There are few situations which can be as picturesque as that of this Island, cut off as it is from the mainland by immense arms of sea, and surrounded by reefs against which the waves break furiously. It is sometimes the refuge of the pallid sailor against the perils of a storm, but more often "La Gorgona" is a dangerous rock on which many vessels have been wrecked.

Exhausted by the storms we had weathered, I immediately went ashore with some of the crew. They had never seen the island before, and did not know if it was inhabited. When we had reached the shore, I used what little strength I had left to reconnoitre the area, and soon convinced myself that no human creature had ever inhabited so sterile an abode.

I was, however, wrong in this, and I soon changed my mind when I caught sight of some walls, half ruined by time. They seemed to have been built several centuries before. Ivy and other shrubs of that species had so overgrown the wall which gave them protection that it was difficult to see the stones.

I had a tent pitched within those walls, where once there had been houses, so that I could spend the night there. The sailors slept on board ship; I found myself alone in the region. This pleasant thought preoccupied me for the first part of the evening. I found myself, so to speak, in a little world, where there were certainly sufficient resources to provide for my well-being: I was protected from the seductions of mankind, their ambitious deceits, and their ephemeral passions. Why should I not live there, if not happily at least wisely and contentedly . . . ?

I fell asleep during this train of thought and as you can imagine, I compared myself with Robinson Crusoe. Like him, I was King of my island. I was still in my first sleep, when I was awakened by startled cries, and by bright torchlight. My astonishment changed to fear when I heard someone shouting in Italian : "Wretch! You will perish . . ."

My only weapon was my cane. I seized it, and flung myself to the foot of my mattress. I looked for the entrance, but found I could not open it. I was deciding what action I should take, when someone set fire to the tent, crying "Thus perish all men". The tone in which this terrible curse was uttered made my blood run cold. I summoned up my courage, however, and, half stifled by clouds of smoke, managed to get clear of the fire, and put myself out of danger. I started looking for the cowardly foe who had sought to sacrifice me so callously, but saw no one and heard not a sound. Picture my situation to yourself :

My heart was still gripped by the danger from which I had just escaped, and alarmed at the risks I might still be running and which I could not foresee . . . I was naked, exposed to the most violent of winds, and the horror of my situation was aggravated still more by the roaring of the waves and the blackness of the night.

By the light of the flames which were consuming my tent I could make out the ruins which I had chosen as my resting place. They seemed to tell me that everything in nature perishes and that I must perish too.

. . . I had not been more than a quarter of an hour in this situation when I heard a noise, and, a moment afterwards, I saw two people arrive. I admit that, because I was unarmed, I hid myself behind a wall while I waited to find out why they were being so cruel : I could not imagine that they would hate mankind so bitterly without some good reason.

Imagine my astonishment when I heard the following words . . . "My daughter, you have brought burning remorse on your father – so near the end of his long life. O God! Listen to the groans of this pitiable wretch. He appeals to the Almighty, who for so many years has watched over our life. My daughter – what have you done? Perhaps you have sacrificed to the ghosts of our compatriots a fellow countryman. Perhaps this was one of those virtuous Englishmen who still protect our exiled citizens ... No, no! My spirit cannot survive this blow. I have endured the sorrows of my country, my family, and my self while innocence held its sway in my heart, but that these white hairs should be sullied by crime ... Farewell, my daughter ... I will atone for your crime. Yes, eager flames, purify ... My daughter, I forgive you. Live to avenge me and never forgive our country's tyrants ... set down to them even this new crime – set down to them the death of your father."

This speech gave me new life. Such situations are difficult to depict. I threw myself at the feet of this virtuous old man, "Yes, my father", I said, "I am an Englishman, and an Englishman who is your friend. What I have just heard consoles me for the regrettable accident which nearly cost me my life". After expressing his obvious delight at this, the old man led me to the cave where he lived. "Welcome, Englishman. You shall be lord here. Virtue has the right to be respected everywhere". I would never finish my story if I wanted to set down all the discussions we held together. I asked him to give me an account of the events which had made him flee the society of men, and he began like this :

I was born in Corsica, and grew up with a violent love for my unfortunate country and for her independence. At that time, we were languishing in the fetters of the Genoese. Although only twenty years old, I was the first to raise the banner of Liberty, and my desperate young arm gained many victories over the tyrants, victories that my compatriots were still praising ten years ago. Several years later, our tyrants applied to the Germans for help. What had we done to the Germans, to make them fight against us? Nevertheless, they were the losers by it, and several times we saw the Imperial

Eagle in full flight before our light-footed mountain-men . . .
The wicked in this world always have friends and the French
came to help them. First the French were defeated, then they
defeated us. The lowlands and the towns surrendered. As for
me, I fled in search of refuge with those of my compatriots who
had sworn not to outlive the freedom of their country.

After various changes of fortune, Paoli di Rostino became
first magistrate and generalissimo. We expelled our tyrants.
We were free, we were happy; then the French, who are often
called enemies of free men, came armed with fire and sword.
In two years they had compelled Paoli to leave and the nation
to surrender.

For my part, I continued to fight, together with my friends
and relatives, for eight years. During this period, I saw forty
of my companions die on the common scaffold. One day we
resolved to have our revenge, and nearly sixty of us came down
from the hills – the remnants of the defenders of liberty.

In the lowlands we took more than one hundred Frenchmen. We were leading them to our hide-out when we were
warned that the tyrants had seized it. I left my men, to fly
to the rescue of my unfortunate father – I found him lying in
a pool of his own blood. He had just enough strength to say
to me : "My son, avenge my death. It is the first law of nature.
It does not matter if you die like me, but you must never recognise the French as your masters". I was continuing on my
way to find out what had happened to my mother, when I
found her naked body in the most revolting position, hideously
disfigured. My wife and three of my brothers had been hanged
on the very same spot. Seven of my sons, three of whom had
not reached the age of five, had met with the same fate. Our
huts had been burned, and the blood of our flocks was ming-
ling with that of my relations. I searched for my daughter, but
I could not find her; furious, distraught, carried away by rage,
I wanted to go and die by the hands of those brigands who
had killed all my people. But I was held back by my companions; we buried all the bodies of our unfortunate relatives,
and we resolved . . . O God! What did we not resolve . . .
But in the end we decided to leave a fated island, which was

ruled by tigers. Our ship put in at "La Gorgona". I found the landscape suited my disposition and I stayed there.

I kept only three muskets and four barrels of powder. My companions set sail again for Italy. I saw their ship leave, and I had no regrets. I had food for three days. I knew that there are few places on earth where a man cannot find nourishment. The walls where you slept are the ruins of an old monastery and the well still exists. The fish, and the small creatures of the sea, the acorns from the holm-oaks that you can see – all these provide me with food. Here, I think of myself as the dictator of a Republic. There are innumerable birds on these rocks, but I never kill them. They are my subjects. In any case, how can I kill them if I never see them? The disasters which have poisoned my days have made the light of the sun unwelcome to me. It never shines for me. I only take the air at night so that my griefs are not renewed by the sight of the mountains where my ancestors once lived free men. The little pine-forest you see over there gives us more wood than we need, and this wood provides our light. We live by the light of these torches. Our expeditions, our fishing trips are lit by this, our sun, which may not be as bright as yours, but at least it only shines on just actions.

A year passed uneventfully; then, at about this time of night, one day in December, I saw some fires near the wall which told me that several men had arrived. I slipped round with as little noise as possible, and I saw seven Turks, who held three men in irons. I saw them release their prisoners, kill one of them, and free the other two, leaving them no food. After this, they returned to ship. When I had convinced myself that the two new arrivals were not French, I decided to give them refuge. With this purpose in mind, I returned to my cave and lit a great fire. Drawn by the light, they soon came to me. Imagine my surprise when I recognised my daughter. Her companion was a young Frenchman. Out of consideration for my daughter, I granted him his life.

"Sir", I said to him, "in future you will recognise that I am an enemy of your nation, and that I have sworn on my altar, by the God they have outraged, to have my revenge, to massacre any Frenchman who falls into my power. I exempt you, however, out of consideration for my daughter. Seek out somewhere to live on this island, far from this place. Come out only when the sun is up. I permit you to live. If you fail in this, you will die."

Three years passed in this way without my ever having the curiosity to see if he was still alive. At the end of this time, I went over there, and could find no trace of his body. I do not know what can have become of him. But I bless Heaven for delivering me from that wicked man.

Six years ago, I was awakened by the sound of cannon and musket fire. The sun was up. I did not want to break my oath, in spite of my strong inclination to do so, and I waited for nightfall. As soon as darkness had spread its black veil, I lit a great fire and set out to make a tour of my kingdom. I saw seven men lying on the ground, stretched out on blankets, and four others who were attending them. The four came at me.

Like a fool, I had not the sense to defend myself. They pulled my beard, struck me, jeered at me, called me a savage. They tried to force me to tell them where they could find water. I refused, to punish them for their ill treatment of me. Besides, they were Frenchmen.

My daughter, who follows me almost everywhere I go, soon arrived. The moment she saw the situation I had been forced into, she shot two of the brigands dead on the spot. The two others fled. Their frigate was quite some distance away. It could not come any closer because of the rocks. I shouted to them to come and rescue the sick men they had left behind. They sent three men who rowed ashore. I permitted them all to embark. O fearful ingratitude! They had no sooner returned to their frigate, than they fired several cannon balls against the remains of the walls, which they took to be my habitation.

Since that time, I have sworn anew on my altar, never to spare another Frenchman. Several years ago, I saw two ships of that nation wrecked. A few good swimmers managed to reach the island, but we put them to death. After helping them as men, we killed them as Frenchmen.

Last year, one of the ships which sails regularly between

Corsica and France ran aground here. The terrible cries of these unfortunate men moved me to pity. Since then, I have often reproached myself for this weakness, but what do you expect, sir? I am a man and before acquiring the heart of a king or a minister, the sentiments which bind us to nature must be stifled : I had only been a king for eleven years.

I thus lit a great fire near the place where they could come ashore and by this means, I saved them. Perhaps you anticipate some description of their gratitude . . . Oh no! These monsters had hardly arrived on shore when they turned on their benefactor. Two troopers were escorting a criminal whom they had left on board . . . I asked what he had done. They replied that he was Corsican scum and that such people all deserve to be hanged. I was furious – but what was to become of me! They recognised me as Corsican, and announced their intention of taking me with them. I was an outlaw who deserved to be broken on the wheel. They did more than just threaten : they put me in irons. They maintained that a reward had been promised for the men who handed me over. I was lost. I was to pay the penalty for my unfortunate weakness, on the scaffold. My angry ancestors were having their revenge for my betrayal of the vengeance I owed to their spirits . . . Nevertheless, heaven beheld my repentance and saved me.

The ship was delayed for seven days. At the end of this period, they were short of water so they needed to know where they could draw some. They had to promise my freedom. They released me : I took advantage of this moment to plunge the dagger of vengeance into the hearts of two of those perfidious men. It was then that I saw nature's sun for the first time. How magnificent it seemed to me, but, O God! how could the sun behold such treachery. Meanwhile, my daughter was on board ship, in irons just as I had been. Fortunately, these brutal men had not realised she was a woman. I had to think of some means of rescuing her. After brooding over the problem for some time, I dressed myself in the uniform of one of the soldiers I had killed. Armed with two pistols which I found on him, with his sabre and with my four daggers, I reached the ship. The Captain and a cabin boy were the first to feel the cold steel of my wrath. The others fell in the same way, bearing the full brunt of my fury. I collected together all the crew's belongings. We dragged their bodies to our altar, and there burned them all. This new incense seemed to please the Deity . . .

PART THREE

Preparations for the Discourse
on Happiness

February to August 1791

Since Napoleon had obtained his commission, he had already spent three long periods of leave in Corsica – from September 15 1786 to September 12 1787, from January 1 1788 to May 30 1788, and from September 1789 to February 1791, a total of nearly three years. During the third period, he had been active in Corsican politics, and had sent an Address to the National Assembly, begging them to "turn your attention to us". When he returned in February, Napoleon travelled on foot from Valence via the village of Serve, to Saint-Vallier. On the way, he wrote down his personal assessment of the political awareness of rural society. On April 1, he was promoted to premier lieutenant, and on June 14, he was transferred from the La Fère Regiment to the 4th Artillery Regiment, stationed at Valence. There, Napoleon again stayed with Mademoiselle Bou, and soon managed to become elected to the organising committee of the local Society of Friends of the Constitution. In this capacity, he condemned Louis XVI's flight to Varennes, and organised the local pledge of allegiance to the National Assembly. Napoleon's reading in Valence was mainly concerned with a prize which had been announced by the Academy of Lyon while he was in Ajaccio earlier in the year. This prize was offered by Raynal, through the Academy, for the best essay on the subject of man's happiness. Napoleon needed the 1200 francs to pay for the education of Louis, his younger brother who was living with him in Valence, and to augment his own meagre pay. The Examining Committee thought his style uncontrolled and clumsy, and did not award him the prize. Napoleon now applied for a further six months' leave, and managed to side-step the official ban on all leave in the current political situation, through the influence of General DuTeil.

Introduction

FROM THE end of May to the beginning of August 1791, Napoleon's notes on history (Machiavelli and Le Noble) and on philosophy (Voltaire) show that he was preparing for his entry to the competition sponsored by the Academy at Lyon. The essay involved a study of the bases of man's happiness – political, moral and personal. Napoleon approached this task seriously : it was a chance to establish his reputation in French literary circles. Rousseau had done precisely that, when he won a competition arranged by the Academy of Dijon, on the subject of the progress of the Arts and Sciences. Napoleon also needed the substantial 1200 franc prize. Most of his writings in this period relate to his preparations for the *Discourse*.

After the flight of Louis XVI in 1791, Napoleon, in his brief essay *Republic or Monarchy,* attacked the royalist orators for their misunderstanding of the political situation. Shortly after this, Napoleon wrote the *Dialogue on Love.* The choice of subject is significant it does not remotely concern the Corsican Independence movement and covers ground that Napoleon had not tackled in depth before. *A Meeting at the Palais Royale* revealed Napoleon's talent for writing dialogue, *A Parallel between love of Glory and love of Country* was supposedly written for a young lady, but the *Dialogue* represents his first sustained attempt to construct an argument around the structure of this form.

When he was writing the *History of Corsica* Napoleon had accused Father Dupuy of taking the "metaphysical content" out of his work by trying to telescope the style. In the *Dialogue*, he mentions the emptiness of "metaphysical definitions" and of "great words" which have no substantial content, in a way that strikingly reflects Dupuy's criticisms. There is no traditional introduction to the work : Napoleon is trying to compress his ideas. The dialogue begins in the middle of a heated discussion between Bonaparte and his friend from the regiment La Fère, Alexander des Mazis. Napoleon had retained the friendship of this young officer, and it is reasonable to assume that the *Dialogue*'s most striking features – a sense of immediacy, of the spoken word, and of realistic character study, are genuinely taken from life. Perhaps Napoleon lost the argument in real life and re-wrote the discussion in terms which justified his side of the question. At Paris, Auxonne and Valence, Napoleon had been noted for his constant need to assert, by "irrefutable proof", the superiority of his position in a given argument. He claimed that he read Plato's *Republic* not for the style of the translation, or for the ideas, but for the way that Socrates handles the other protagonists. In the *Dialogue on Love* he allows Des Mazis to defend his position thoroughly, then destroys what has just been said, with a barrage of social and political theories. Napoleon obviously tried hard to adapt his style to the personalities of the two people in the dialogue. Hakem and the Old Corsican had been clearly defined characters, but Des Mazis' style – impatient, self-indulgent, immature – which clearly contrasts with Napoleon's taciturn mastery of the situation, represents an improvement in his technique as a writer (see Tomiche op. cit.).

A page from Napoleon's private journal, dated February 8 1791, contains a different definition of love.

> What is love? All the seasons suit it, everything in nature inspires it . . . it is in the thickets of Italy, the forests of the Ardennes, under the sign of the Lion, or under that of the Bear. What is love? A sentiment of his own inadequacy, which quickly possesses the solitary, or isolated man – it is both a sentiment of weakness, and of immortality. The soul . . . takes on a new strength, tears of pleasure begin to flow . . . that is love! (quoted in Tomiche op. cit.).

The *Dialogue on Love* may just have been an intellectual game, an attempt to vary a limited prose style by creating two different attitudes towards sentiment. On board the flagship *Orient,* on his way to Egypt, Napoleon played a similar game: two officers would be chosen, each would be given a point of view to defend, and Napoleon would act as referee. The officer who sustained an argument in favour of the most difficult position of the two would win. (See Tomiche, op. cit.)

At the same time, Napoleon was busily writing down a series of polysyllabic words which might come in useful for the forthcoming essay prize, and which were calculated to impress the examiners. He discovered who the "Ichthyophages" and the "Rhizophages" were, what a "bibliographie" was, the symbolic significance of a "tulipe". From William Coxe's *Travels in Switzerland*, and also possibly from the *Encyclopédie* and *La Nouvelle Héloïse*, he listed a series of technical terms for use when describing mountains. One interesting entry in this section is "Crétins : espèce d'imbéciles que l'on trouve dans le Valais". Diderot's and d'Alembert's *Encyclopédie* contained an article entitled "Crétins" which described the people of the Valais region as a subnormal, in-bred community. Rousseau wrote his letter on the Valais in *La Nouvelle Héloïse* as an attack on this article : he had been planning a history of the region for some years, and may have been offended at not being asked to contribute to this section of the *Encyclopédie*. Napoleon was possibly alluding to this controversy here, although the note may have been indirectly suggested by a reading of Coxe.

Most of the words and definitions that Napoleon prepared appear in *Discourse* at one time or another. Sometimes – in the case of "Ichthyophages" for example – they appear for no logical reason, and the ruse becomes transparent.

Napoleon then started to write a series of rough drafts : they consist of fragments of sentences, unfinished and unpolished. Their style is self-conscious and mannered; Napoleon is evidently trying hard to achieve some literary elegance. He eventually succeeds with the aid of whole phrases taken from eighteenth-century philosophers such as Condillac and Diderot. By August 1791, Napoleon had completed his preparations, and had, according to Méneval's *Mémoires*, already written a full-length version of the *Discourse* which "lacked the final touches".

But in spite of the comprehensive reading-list, which included dictionaries, travellers' tales, works by political and moral theorists and histories, Napoleon answered the Academy's essay question less as a philosopher than as a romantic novelist. He defines none of his terms, he constructs no theories – instead he bases his argument on imaginary examples, dialogues and situations. An adolescent discusses injustice with a priest, a lawyer and a wise old man. The various meanings of the word "senti-ment" are discussed with reference to the impact of landscape and architecture on the senses. Instead of constructing a theoreti-cal treatise on this issue, based on Rousseau's projected *Morale Sensitive ou le Matérialisme du Sage,* (described in detail in the *Confessions*) Napoleon gives long descriptions of St. Peter's in Rome, a trip to the mountains, his return to Corsica after so many years in France, and the pleasures of indulging in solitary "rêveries". He writes that he will define the "sentimental organ-isation of man" : he does so by giving romantic accounts of a young girl dying of love, and a rhapsodic description of a pretty landscape. He leaves it up to the reader to define the concept with reference to the impressions caused by these images. Méneval, in his *Mémoires,* summarises Napoleon's style in the *Discourse.*

In order to give a *picturesque* definition of sentiment, the author of the discourse takes his reader on a tour of the sites most favourable to meditation : these are depicted sometimes in bold outline, sometimes with descriptive detail. He trans-ports him from the shepherd's hut to the church of St. Peter in Rome, and describes the impressions that the traveller experiences when he first enters the immense basilica. (Quoted in Tomiche op. cit.)

The third part of the *Discourse,* where Napoleon tackles the subject of rationalism, and its place in the "human organisation" has pretensions to containing a more clearly defined, logically constructed argument. But when he takes the discussion on to a political plane, the *Discourse* dissolves into a mass of ill-digested, half remembered ideas from *Du Contrat Social,* with examples from Plutarch, interspersed with clumsy compliments to the examiners. When Napoleon actually starts *defining* his political maxims, the *Discourse* goes to pieces. Only when Napoleon is writing from his personal experiences of frustrated patriotism, wounded amour-propre and nostalgic recollection does he show his talent as a writer. Not surprisingly, he did not win the prize.

Republic or Monarchy

FOR SOME time now, my tastes have led me to occupy myself with public affairs. If an unprejudiced writer on politics could ever have had doubts as to whether he should prefer Republicanism or Monarchism, I think that by now his doubts must have been allayed. Republicans are insulted, slandered and threatened, and the only reason given is that Republicanism is impossible in France.

In fact, Monarchist orators have contributed greatly to the fall of the monarchy, because after wasting so much breath on vain analysis, they still say that a Republican government is impossible because it is impossible. I have read all the speeches of the monarchist orators; I see in them great efforts to support a lost cause. They wander off into assertions which they do not prove; really, if I had any doubts, reading their speeches would have dissipated them. Twenty-five million inhabitants cannot live together in a republic, they say.

Without mores (manners), there can be no republic. They say "A great nation needs a centre of unity. Twenty five million men cannot live together in a Republic". That is an unpolitical adage.

Dialogue on Love

DES MAZIS. What, monsieur! You ask me what love is? Are you so different from other men then?

BONAPARTE. I am not asking you for a definition of love. I was in love once, and I can remember enough of it not to need those metaphysical definitions which do nothing but confuse matters: I am doing more than denying its existence. I think it is harmful to society, to the individual happiness of men, in short I think that love does harm . . . and that it would be a benevolent action of some protective divinity to rid us of it and to deliver the world.

DES MAZIS. What! Love harmful to society, love which gives life to the whole of nature, the source of everything creative and of all happiness. If there was no love, sir, we might as well not exist!

BONAPARTE. You are getting over-heated. Passion is carrying you away. Please remember that I am your friend. Don't look on me with indignation and tell me why you do not see your old friends any more since this passion has dominated you. What has become of your usual occupations? Why are you neglecting your relatives and friends? Your whole day is given over to your monotonous and solitary wandering until such time as you can see Adelaide.

DES MAZIS. Oh! what do your occupations and acquaintances matter to me, sir? What is the point of half-digested science? What concern is it of mine what happened a thousand years ago? What influence can I have on the course of the stars? What do the minute details of men's puerile discussions matter to me? . . . Doubtless I used to concern myself with these things. I had nothing better to do. I had to find some means of warding off the boredom which threatened me; but, believe me, seated in my study, I knew the emptiness of my heart. Sometimes my mind was satisfied, but my sentiments! Oh God! I was only vegetating until I fell in love. Nowadays, on the other hand, when dawn tears me from slumber, I no longer say "Why does the sun shine for me today?" No! the first ray of light shows me Adelaide dressed for the morning. I imagine her thinking of me, smiling at me. Yesterday evening, she pressed my hand; she sighed, our eyes met. How well they expressed our sentiments! I gaze on her portrait; it ravishes my soul. A hundred times I put it down only to pick it up again. This wandering, sir, that you call monotonous, oh! no, the entire world could not contain more variety. First I go over all the things she has said to me; I read the letter she wrote; I wonder who could paint the extent of my love. I do this a hundred times over. My imagination awakes; I see my passion crowned; sometimes I regret that I do not have an immense fortune to sacrifice to her . . . Everything connected with her is sacred to me. Sometimes I think about the preparations for the wedding which will soon unite us, even down to the presents I shall give her. My heart swells imagining some glorious deed which will serve her and prove my love. Think of the château where we will spend our days – the sombre thickets, the laughing fields, the delicious flower-beds. I care for nothing but the pleasure of being beside her every day. Soon she will give me the proofs of her love . . . But you are laughing! Honestly, I detest you.

BONAPARTE. I am laughing at the great problems which seem to possess your mind, and even more at the fire with which you communicate them to me. What strange sickness has got hold of you? I feel that the reason which I am going to bring in to help you will have no effect. In your current delirium, not only will you close your ears to it, you will despise it. Remember that you do not have a level head and that my friendship was ever the judge that recalled you to your duty. Remember that I have always proved myself worthy of friendship. In your delirious state, I will have to remind you of your obligations to me, and of the proofs of my sentiments which you know very well, otherwise I myself will not be safe from your invective in the height of your delirium. You are like a sick man who sees nothing but the chimera he is chasing, without being aware of the sickness which has caused it or the health he has lost. So I won't discuss whether your pleasures are worthy of a man, or even whether they are manly. I am prepared to believe that our sex, which rules the world because of its strength, industry, spirit and other natural faculties, finds its supreme felicity in languishing in the fetters of an effeminate passion, under the sway of a being weaker in mind as in body. I am prepared to believe what you say, that the memory of your Adelaide, her image and her conversation can distract you from your usual occupations and friends – but is it not true that you are always seeking an end to this state and that your insatiable imagination wishes you to acquire what Adelaide's virtue cannot grant you? My calm detachment, I can see, is not qualified to describe the heavy burden which torments the existence of a lover whenever he meets the slightest set-back. If Adelaide went away even for a fortnight what would become of you? If somebody else attempts to please the girl you think belongs to you, what anxiety! If a nervous mother objects to your too-frequent visits because malicious people are talking, in short, sir, I don't know – a hundred other little things which can really upset a lover are agitating you. Nights go by without any sleep, your meals without any food. The earth is not large enough to contain your extreme anxiety. Your blood boils, you stride about with a distracted look on your face. Poor Chevalier, is that happiness? I have no doubt that though today in the ecstasy that a squeeze of the hand has brought you, you find this state supremely happy, I have no doubt, I say, that tomorrow in a different mood you would find this feebleness insupportable.

But, Chevalier, your position is this. If the country was attacked and needed to be defended, what would you do? Is there anything you are good for? Would anyone entrust the happiness of his fellow-men to a child who cries incessantly, who alarms himself or rejoices when someone else so much as moves? Would anyone entrust state secrets to someone who has no will of his own?

DES MAZIS. Always grand words without any sense to them. What do your state and its secrets matter to me? Truly, I cannot follow you at all today. You have never argued so pitiably!

BONAPARTE. Ah, Chevalier, what do you care about your fellow citizens, the state, society! These are the consequences of a heart which has grown too lax, abandoned to sensual pleasures. There is no strength or virtue in the course you are taking. Once your only ambition was to do good, but today this very good means nothing to you. So what is this vicious sentiment which has taken the place of your love for virtue? All you want is to live unknown in the shade of your poplars. Profound philosophy! Ah! Chevalier, I detest this passion which has produced such a complete change in you. You cannot see that you are verging on egotism, and that nothing matters to you : men's opinions, the esteem of your friends, the love of your relatives – everything is subjugated to the strong tyrant of your weakness. A glance, a squeeze of the hand, a kiss, Chevalier, and what do the troubles of your country matter then, or the bad opinion of your friends; bodily contact . . . but I do not want to irritate you. I am willing to believe that love has incomparable pleasures, pains still greater, perhaps, but no matter – let us consider only the influence it has on society. It is true, Chevalier, that we are born to be happy, that this is the supreme law that nature has engraved deeply in our being. It is true that this is the foundation which has been given to serve as a guide to our conduct. Each man, born judge of what suits him, has the right to dispose of his body and his affections, but this state of independence is in fact inconsistent with the state of servitude to which society has led us.

In changing condition, we had therefore to change our attitudes. It was necessary to substitute for the cry of sentiment that of prejudice. That is the basis of all social institutions. It was necessary to take man, right from the start, and make a completely different creature of him, if possible. Do you think that without this change so many men would allow themselves to be humbled by a small number of great noblemen, and that their sumptuous palaces would be respected by men who have no bread to eat? Strength is the law of animals, conviction the law of men. They acknowledged, either to put off the attacks of stronger animals, or in order not to be subjected to constant fighting among themselves, they acknowledged, I say, laws of property, and each man was assured in the name of all of the ownership of his land.

This agreement only existed between a small number of men. So they needed magistrates, both to repulse the attacks of neighbouring peoples, and to make sure the accepted agreement was put into practice.

These magistrates took increasing pleasure in giving orders, but the most vigilant members of the public resisted them. They in turn were won over, and in this way became party to the projects of ambitious men. The people were subjugated. You can see inequality quickly creeping in. You can see the ruling class being formed from the ruled. Religion came to console the unhappy men who found themselves stripped of all property. It came to enslave them for ever. Men no longer ruled their lives by the clamour of conscience. No! they feared that a sentiment which they were doing everything in their power to stifle would take the upper hand.

So then there was a God. This God came to govern the world. Everything was done by acts of His will. He had given written laws . . . and the empire of the priests began, an empire which will probably have no end.

It is sad but true that man was degraded in this way, but none can deny that the state of society is legitimate. Man's silence on this point is a tacit sign of approval which is irrefutable. You are twenty years old, sir, choose : either renounce your rank, your fortune and leave a world you hate, or enrolling yourself in the ranks of its citizens, submit to its laws. You enjoy the advantages of the contract, will you renounce the other clauses? I could not believe you an honest man if I even wondered. So you ought to be attached to a state which brings you so much well-being, and while endeavouring to make a worthy use of the advantages it has accorded you, you should at the same time work for the happiness of your inferiors and ensure the prosperity of the society which has singled you out. To do this, my dear Chevalier, you ought always to be master of yourself and your actions, and you must not allow the appearance of things to put you off . . . In order to do this you must be guided by the light of reason and give some thought to the rights of those to whom you are indebted. To do this you must be ready to undertake anything of service to the state, whether it be as a soldier, a business man, a courtier even, if the interest of the people and your nation demand it. Ah! your reward will be sweet! Then you can challenge the malicious hysteria of calumny and jealousy! You can fearlessly challenge time itself! Your decrepit limbs may no longer be anything but an imperfect image of what they once were, yet they will inspire the respect of all those who come near you. One man will recount, in his hut, the relief you brought him. Another as he recounts the story of the plots against him will say, "If he had not come to my rescue, I would have perished on the common scaffold". Chevalier, cease to confine your noble mind and your heart, once so proud, into so restricted a sphere. You—at a woman's feet! You—scorning the hardships of man! Sooner crush your sense of honour! Esteemed by your fellow men, respected and loved by your vassals, death will take you in the midst of the tears of those who surround you, after you have spent a tranquil life, considered an oracle by your friends and a father by your vassals.

DES MAZIS. I do not understand you. How, sir, could my love prevent me from following the scheme you have just sketched out? What idea can you have of Adelaide?

If virtue means doing one's duty, if duty means relieving the unfortunate, if virtue means loving one's country, mankind and society, who is more virtuous than Adelaide? Do you think I could do good with the coldness of philosophy? When Adelaide's will is the incentive which drives me on, when pleasing her is my reward . . . No, sir, you have never been in love.

BONAPARTE. I pity your mistake. What, Chevalier, you think

that love is the path of virtue? It encumbers you at every step. Be sincere. Since this fatal passion has troubled your peace, have you even thought of any other delight than that of love. Clearly you will do good or evil according to the symptoms of your passion. But, what am I saying? You and your passion are part of one and the same being. While it lasts, you will act only in its interests, and since you have agreed that the duties of a rich man are to do good, to rescue the unfortunate men who groan in their poverty, that the duties of a man of birth oblige him to use the influence of his name to overthrow the intrigues of the wicked, that the duties of the citizen are to defend the country and to contribute to its prosperity, will you not admit that the duties of a good son are to be grateful to his father for the benefits of a good education, to his mother . . . No! Chevalier, I will be silent if I have to prove such obvious points to you.

Corsica in the Eighteenth Century

e dwelt so much on the charms of his native country, which, from his early recollection,
to him superior to any other spot in the world" (Las Cases, reporting a conversation
with Napoleon on St. Helena).

Napoleon with his fellow cadets at the military preparatory school, Brienne.
'hen he first came to the College, he spoke only the Corsican dialect . . . he was
markable for the dark colour of his complexion . . . and for his piercing, scrutinising
glance" (Bourrienne).

Désirée Clary, youngest daughter of a Marseilles textile millionaire, who nearly became Madame Bonaparte. The love affair may have inspired parts of the story of "Clisson and Eugénie", although Désirée had more in common with "Amélie" than "Eugénie".

Napoleon watches, and takes notes on the massacre at the Tuileries, August 10th 1792.
"If Louis XVI had appeared on horseback, victory would have been his".

Major Bonaparte commands the siege batteries at Toulon, December 1793.
"I have commenced my Memoirs with the Siege of Toulon" wrote Napoleon on $\therefore$
Helena, *"I do not consider my actions before that date as belonging to history".*

Discourse to the Academy
of Lyon[*]

. . . FIRST IT is essential to settle our ideas on happiness.

Man is born to be happy; nature, that enlightened mother, has endowed him with all the necessary organs from his creation. Happiness is nothing but the pursuit of a life which conforms most closely to nature's organisation.

Men of all climates, sects and religions, are there any among you who are prevented by the prejudices of their dogmas from listening to evidence on this principle? Well, let them put their right hand on their hearts, their left hand on their eyes, and examine their conscience. Let them be of good faith . . . and contradict me if they can.

We must live in a manner which conforms to our organisation, or no happiness.

Our animal organisation has some indispensable needs : to eat, to sleep, to procreate. Food, shelter, clothes and a woman are therefore strictly necessary for happiness.

Our intellectual organisation has no less imperious appetites, whose satisfaction is even more precious. It is on their fullest development that happiness really depends. To feel and to reason, these are the attributes of mankind, these are his claims to the supremacy he has acquired, which he has kept, and will ever keep.

Our sentiments revolt against discomfort and make us friends of beauty and of justice, enemies of the oppressor and the wicked. It is in our sentiment that our conscience lies, and therefore morality . . . Woe to the man to whom these truths are not

* Discourse on the Question set by the Academy of Lyon : What Sentiments and What Truths should be inculcated in Men for their Happiness?

apparent. He will find nothing in life but rejection, he will know no other pleasures than those of the senses.

To reason is to compare, perfection grows from reasoning like fruit from the tree. Reason, ever-present judge and censor of our actions, ought to be the invariable guide to them. The eyes of reason protect man from the precipices of passion, as its decisions modify even the sentiment of man's rights. Sentiment gives birth to society, reason maintains it.

It is therefore necessary to eat, sleep, procreate, feel and reason in order to live like a man, and hence to be happy.

Of all the lawgivers, whom the esteem of their fellow-citizens has called on to legislate for them, none seem to have been more penetrated by those truths than Lycurgus and M. Paoli. Very different paths, however, led them to put these truths into practice.

The Lacedemonians had abundant nourishment, comfortable clothes and houses, and robust wives. They reasoned in their gatherings, their government was a free one, they rejoiced in their strength, dexterity, glory, the esteem of their compatriots, and the prosperity of their country : these were the satisfactions of their sentiments. They were tender to their wives, moved by the varied perspectives of the beautiful landscape of Greece; however, it was principally the spectacle of strength and virtue that moved them. Virtue consists of courage and of strength. Energy is the life of the soul, as it is the principal source of strength for reason.

The heartbeats of a Spartan were those of a strong man, and a strong man is a good one; only the weak man is evil. The Spartan lived therefore in conformity with his organisation. He was happy . . . but all this is now nothing but a dream.

To lead men towards happiness, must they be equal in means? To what extent should one preach to them and impress on them the doctrine of discretionary equality?

Since one must feel in order to be happy, what are the sentiments one should inspire in them?

What are the truths which one should develop in them?

Either you must reason, you say, or you cannot be happy.

PART ONE

When man is born, he brings with him the right to that portion of the fruits of the earth necessary to his existence. After the giddiness of youth comes the dawn of passion; he chooses from among the companions of his games she who will be the companion of his destiny. His vigorous arm, together with his needs, demands work. He casts a glance around him. He sees the land shared between a few owners, serving to feed luxury and superfluity; he asks himself "What are the claims of these men? Why does the idle man own everything, the working man practically nothing? Why, in fact, have they left nothing for me, who have a wife, an aged mother and father to support?"

He seeks out the minister, in whom he places his confidence, and tells him of his doubts. "Man", replies the priest, "never reflect on the existence of society. God leads us all: abandon yourself to his providence . . . this life is nothing but a voyage . . . things are determined by a justice whose decrees we must not seek to understand . . . Believe, obey, never reason, and work: these are your duties".

A noble spirit, a tender heart and a natural reason cannot be satisfied with this reply. He takes his doubts and anxieties elsewhere. He arrives at the house of the wisest man in the district: a lawyer . . . "Wise man", he says, "they have shared out the fruits of the land and given nothing to me!" The wise man laughs at his simplicity, takes him into his study and there from act to act, from contract to contract, from will to will, he proves the legitimacy of the distribution of which the young man complains. "What! are these the claims of those gentlemen?" he cries indignantly. "Mine are more sacred, more universal. They are renewed with my sweat, circulated with my blood, and are written on my nerves and in my heart. They are the necessity of my existence and above all of my happiness!" With these words he seizes all the bits of paper and throws them in the flames.

He soon fears the arm of that Power known as Justice: he takes refuge in his hut to throw himself, distraught, on to the ice-cold body of his father. This respectable man, blinded and crippled by age, seems to be still alive only by some oversight of Death. "My father, you have given me life, and with it a strong instinct for happiness. Well, my father, the ravishers have shared it all out between them, they have only left me my arms because they could not take them from me. Ah, my father, I am thus condemned to continual labour, the most degrading slavery. In the sun of August as in the frosts of January, there will never be any rest for your son. As a reward for such great labour, others will reap the harvest gained by the sweat of my brow! . . . Ah, if only I could provide everything. I will have to feed, house, clothe and keep warm an entire family; bread will be short, my heart will break at every moment, my sensibility will be dulled, my reason blunted; oh, my father, I shall be stupefied, miserable, perhaps even wicked: I shall be unhappy! Was I born for this?"

"My son", replies the venerable old man, "the sacred character of nature is traced in your heart in all its energy: keep it always and you will live happy and strong, but listen carefully to what eighty years of experience have taught me. My son, I have raised you in my arms, I have protected your youthful years, and today when your heart begins to palpitate, your muscles are accustomed to work – but to a moderate labour, which refreshes the body, excites the sentiment, and calms the ardent imagination. My son, have you ever wanted for anything? Your clothing is coarse, your abode is rustic, your food is simple, but once more I ask, have you ever wanted for anything? Your sentiments are pure, like your sensations and like yourself. You needed a wife: my son, you have chosen one. I helped you with my experience to decide your young heart. Oh, my dear friend, why do you complain? You fear the future . . . do as you always have done and you will not need to fear it.

"My son, if I had been one of those unhappy men who

possess nothing, I would have fashioned your body to bear a yoke, like an animal. I would have stifled your feelings and ideas myself. I would have made of you merely the leading animal on your farm. Bowed under the yoke of habit, you would have lived tranquil in your apathy, content with your ignorance. You would not have been happy, oh no, you would not, but you would have died without knowing whether you had lived; because as you have pointed out, my son, in order to live you must be able to feel and reason, furthermore you must not be overwhelmed by physical need. Yes, good young man, let this news refresh you, console you and calm your anxieties; these fields, this hut, these animals are ours. I wanted to leave you in ignorance: it is so pleasant and sweet to climb, so hard to fall.

"Soon your father will no longer be of this world. He has lived long enough, he has known true pleasure; he has known the greatest of all pleasures, since he can still press you against his breast. One thing, my son, if you wish to imitate him! You have an ardent spirit, but your work, your wife, that gentle gift of love, your children, how many objects surround you to fill the emptiness of your heart. Guard yourself only against the greed for riches. Riches have no influence on happiness, my son, except to provide or deny one's physical necessity. You have what is necessary. In addition, you are accustomed to work. You are the richest in the district. Learn therefore to bridle your imagination. From an ardent imagination to an unruly spirit, my son, there is only reason between.

"Are rich people happy? My son, they can be, but no more than you. I say they can be, you understand, because they rarely are. Happiness comes especially to someone in your position and your state, because it belongs to reason and sentiment. The state of a rich man is that of an empire of unbridled imagination, vanity, the pleasures of the senses, of caprices and fantasies. Don't ever envy it, and if you are ever offered all the riches of the country, my only friend, cast them from you, unless you accept them to share them immediately with your fellow citizens.

But, my son, that act of strength and magnanimity belongs only to a god. Be a man, but be truly a man. Be master of yourself : without strength, my son, there is no virtue or happiness".

These are the two ends of the current social chain. Yes gentlemen, I agree that the rich man should be at the top; but there should be no miserable wretches at the bottom. There should only be the small landowner, the little merchant, or the skilled artisan, who with a moderate amount of labour can feed, clothe and house his family. You must therefore recommend the lawgiver not to promulgate a civil code where a few people can possess everything, but to resolve his political problem so that the lowest will have something. He need not establish equality; the two extremes are so far removed, the latitude is so wide that inequality can exist in the intermediate stage. In the hut as in the palace, clad in skins or in fineries from Lyon, at the frugal table of Cincinnatus as at that of Vitellius, man can be happy. It is still necessary that he should possess this hut, these skins and this frugal table. How can the lawgiver influence this? How can he resolve this political problem so that the lowest shall have something? I know of no man who has solved the problem better than M. Paoli . . .

PART TWO

What is sentiment? It is the bond of life, society, love and friendship. It is sentiment which unites the son to the mother, the citizen to his country, it is powerful, above all, in a man of nature. Dissipation and pleasures of the senses blunt its delicacy, but in misfortune man rediscovers it – the agent of consolation which abandons us only with our life.

Are you not yet satisfied? Climb one of the peaks of Mont Blanc, watch the sun as it gradually rises carrying consolation and hope into the ploughman's cottage. Let its first ray enter you heart, and remember well the sensations you experience.

Go down to the seashore, watch the day-star in its decline sinking majestically into the bosom of infinity. Melancholy will master you : you will abandon yourself to it. One cannot resist the melancholy of nature.

Have you ever stood beneath the monument of Saint-Rémy? Have you contemplated its majesty? Transporting your imagination to past ages, the finger of those proud Romans traced over two thousand years ago will make you exist with Aemilius, Scipio and Fabius. Return to yourself to see the mountains distantly shrouded in black cloud crowning the immense plain of Tarascon, where a hundred thousand of the Cimbri are buried. The Rhône flows on one side, more swiftly than an arrow, the little town some distance away, a flock grazing : you are dreaming, no doubt. It is the dream of sentiment.

Lose yourself in the countryside, take refuge in the shepherd's miserable hut. Spend the night there, sleeping on skins, the fire at your feet. What a situation! Midnight sounds, all the beasts of the neighbourhood go out to pasture, their bleating mingles with the voice of the herdsman. It is midnight, do not forget that. What a moment to withdraw into yourself and meditate on the origin of nature, while savouring its most exquisite delights.

Returning from a long walk, have you ever been surprised by nightfall? Have you, by the light of silver rays, reached the perfect silence of the universe? You have been overcome by the heat of the dog-days. You savour the delights of coolness and the salutary balm of rêverie.

Has your family gone to bed, the lights extinguished but not the fire, because the January frost is biting into the vegetation in your garden? What do you do there for a couple of hours? I do not suppose that you are carried away by the rage of ambition or riches. What do you do? You rejoice in yourself.

You know that the cathedral of Saint Peter in Rome is as large as a town. There is a lamp in front of the high altar. You go in at ten in the evening, feel your way forward . . . the feeble light permits you to see nothing but itself. You think you have only just walked in; it is already dawn. It comes in through the windows. The pale morning succeeds the shadowy night. You notice at last and leave. You have been there for six hours. If

I could write down your thoughts, how they would interest a moralist!

Has curiosity, the mother of life, ever made you set sail for Greece? Have you ever been forced by the currents to put in at the island of Monte-Cristo? Two hours of the night remain to you. You seek refuge, you have soon explored this little rock. You find in the middle, on a height, the remains of an old monastery. Behind a fragment of wall, which is covered by creeper and rosemary, you have your tent pitched. The harsh roar of the waves that break on the rocks, for this vast expanse of sea surrounds you, will give you some idea of how terrible this element can be for the defenceless traveller. A thin canvas, and a wall more than fifteen centuries old shelter you : you are agitated by sentiment.

Have you ever been out in your flowering thickets or in a vast forest at seven in the morning in the fruit season? Have you ever slept in a grotto surrounded by the waters of the Dryads, in the height of the dog-days? You will be able to pass whole hours alone without being able to tear yourself away, or having to put up with the chatter of irritating people who come to importune you.

There is no man who has not experienced the sweetness, the melancholy, the thrill, which most of these situations inspire. How sorry I would be for anyone who could not understand me and who had never been moved by the electricity of nature. If sentiment did no more than make us feel these delicious emotions, it would have already done much for us. It would already have offered us a succession of pleasures without regrets, without fatigue, without any type of violent emotion. That would have been its most precious gift, if love of country, conjugal love and divine friendship had not also been part of its liberal gifts.

Return to your country after six years' absence : you will wander around sites which were theatres of the scenes of your youth and witnesses of the agitation which the first knowledge of men and the dawn of passion produce in our senses. You will re-live for a moment the life of your infancy, and you will rejoice in its pleasures. You will feel all the flames of love for your country. You have, you say, a father and a tender mother, inno-cent sisters, brothers who are your friends as well; too happy man, run, fly, do not lose a moment. If death had struck you down on the way, you would not have known the delights of life, those of sweet remembrance, tender respect, and sincere friendship. But, you say, I have a wife and children . . . A wife and children! . . . That is too much, my friend, too much. Never go away; pleasure could suffocate you on your return, or grief overwhelm you on your departure. A wife and child! A father and mother, brothers and sisters, a friend! And we complain of nature and demand to know why we were born! We suffer transitory set-backs with impatience, and run furiously after the emptiness of vanity and riches! What, oh unfortunate humans, is the depraving drink which has so altered the inclinations writ-ten in your blood, in your nerves and in your eyes? . . . Even if you had a spirit as ardent as the heart of Etna, if you have a father, wife and children you need never fear the anxieties of boredom.

Yes, these are the true, the only pleasures of life, from which nothing can distract us and nothing indemnify us. Man may well surround himself with all the trappings of fortune, but as soon as his sentiment takes flight from his heart, boredom pos-sesses it, sadness, black melancholy and despair succeed each other, and if this state continues he kills himself.

Potaveri was uprooted from Tahiti: brought to Europe, he was overwhelmed by care and attention. Nothing was neg-lected that could distract him. A sole object struck him, drew tears of grief from him : it was a tree which also grew in Tahiti. He embraced it passionately, crying, "Tree from my country, tree from my country!" . . . In vain the Court of Copenhagen lav-ished on five Greenlanders everything they could offer them. Anxiety for their country and their families led them to melan-choly and thence to death. If you want another example, how many Englishmen, Dutchmen and Frenchmen have lived with savages! These unfortunate people were reviled in Europe, lived as toys of passion and as sad victims of great men, while the man of nature lives happily in the bosom of sentiment and natural reason.

We have just seen how, by sentiment, we can rejoice in ourselves, in nature, in our country and in the men around us. All we need to observe now is how it makes us tremble at the aspect of the different vicissitudes of life. Here we will convince ourselves that if it makes us friends of beauty and justice, it makes us revolt against the oppressor and the wicked.

A young beauty has just entered her sixteenth year. The roses of her complexion have given way to lilies. Her eyes sparkle no more. Her lively grace has given way to the languor of melancholy. She is in love. Does this inspire in you respect and affection? That is the respect and affection of sentiment. Does she inspire in you scorn for her weakness? Very well! But don't ever tell me so if you value my esteem.

Nina was in love : her beloved died. She should have died too; she survived him however, and remained faithful to him. Nina knew very well that her beloved was dead; but her sentiment could not conceive of his loss. She waited for him. She will wait for him for ever. Do you scorn her folly, hard man? Or do you feel instead esteem for her constancy, tenderness for her loss? That is the esteem and tenderness of sentiment.

An adored wife is dead; the wife of your enemy. The unfortunate man is overcome : he has fled the society of men. Black drapes have replaced the tapestries of gaiety : there are two candles on his table, and despair in his heart. He will spend the rest of his days languishing in this way. Good soul, you feel your hatred fading. You rush to the tomb to bestow on him the marks of your reconciliation. That is the reconciliation of sentiment.

A wretched man groans in fetters. You are aware of his innocence and of the oppressor who keeps him there. You meet the latter in the street. Your eyes blaze, your heart swells, every nerve in your body quivers . . . That is the indignation of sentiment.

You have read Tacitus. Which of you has not cried with young

Cato, "Give me a sword to kill this monster!" For two thousand years the tales of the actions of Sulla, Marius, Nero, Caligula, Domitian etc. have revolted you. They are remembered with hatred and execration. The odious spectacle of crime prospering, or of innocence in fetters breaks your heart. Discouragement circulates in your veins and soon kindles in them the desire for vengeance. If the redeemers of these nations should appear in front of you, you would prostrate yourselves in front of them, and would offer up incense to them. That is the cult of sentiment.

If Socrates draws respect and tears from you, you will want to enrol yourself straightaway in Thrasybules' ranks. Your desperate arm will no longer recognise danger, and you will give yourself no peace until the thirty Tyrants are expelled from Athens.

Caesar, succumbing to twenty-two blows of the dagger, reminds you of the ravaged world, the violated laws, the overthrown republic. You walk by Brutus' side, you follow him to the Capitol. In all his trials you make your body a shield for him. Finally when he perishes at Philippi you cry in a moment of grief, "Virtue, can you be nothing but a chimera?" When stoic Cato disembowels himself so as not to survive the republic, the loss of Rome, and of liberty, I feel proud of my species. The spectacle of this strength uplifts me, I fall prostrate at the foot of his statue. This admiration is the pride, the dignity of sentiment.

The Corsican slaves who were sold in Rome after the victory of C. Ciceraus, were unmoved. They hardened themselves against ill treatment. Nothing could be obtained from them by force. That is man's true character. Has he not reason and sentiment? Is violence used against him? Do tyrants maltreat him? Well, let him die sooner than render any service to his executioner.

How many things could I recount; how many pictures, how many variations could I attempt to draw! But we must stop here. There are truths that should only be half-seen. There is no reader who cannot supply his own. Whoever has a heart, blood in his veins, and is not crushed by the overthrow of morality can conceive of many which are far better than I can depict.

. . . Music is born with men and like most of the arts reaches its perfection with society, is corrupted with society, and is regenerated with society. Music is at one and the same time a gift of sentiment and a means of regulating it. In all ages and every situation, even among animals, music consoles, rejoices and moves men agreeably. When the little bird sings, the labourer mingles his rustic voice with it. His heart swells, and whether he is singing of his love, his desires, his unhappiness, his work and along with it the burden of his labours, he feels himself refreshed. Let us not therefore proscribe music, this tender companion of the man of feeling, this inspiration of sentiment. Let music increase the number of its delights, and may man, savouring little by little the charms of melody, convince himself more deeply of the joys of sentiment, the happiness of country life, and the innocence of the golden age. Let the ambitious man who exerts himself over speculation be moved by it; may the libertine feel, be penetrated by the horror of his excesses, may the heart of the financier and the powerful man be softened. Let sentiment's pearls fall from their eyes. Let the daughter who has gone astray run back to her mother's bosom, to open her heart to her and restore herself to her confidence. Let men in all their vicissitudes remain virtuous! The tones of music can produce this miracle. The absence of virtue is only that of natural sentiment : all that can restore man to it should be precious to the moralist.

Listen to the song of the nightingale or the plaintive laments of a young beauty. See "The Village Cunning Man", that masterpiece of music, or rather of natural sentiment. Have no fear that your heart will be softened by the tears you have shed. Oh, no! it is the song of virtue which has caused them to fall. You will return stronger and more sensitive to feeling, after rejoicing in the tenderness of the simple village girl.

Oh, Rousseau, why did you live for only sixty years! In the interests of virtue you should have been immortal, but had you created nothing but "The Village Cunning Man" you would have done a great deal for the happiness of your fellow men, enough to merit a statue from the grateful world.

There are few interpreters so privileged : it is true there are a great number of fine pieces which one could not play and teach the people too much, but how many are there that should be proscribed? How many are there that inspire nothing but weakness? How many are there which tend only to excite the unbridled appetite? They are like the voice of the Sirens, captivating for a moment, only to deal the death-blow to virtue and happiness straightaway. These masterpieces, this depraving music should be thrown into the fire. They have done more harm to the nations of the world than have the epicurean or the materialist, for these latter have only found so many proselytes because sentiment itself had already undergone an alteration.

When illness manifests itself in the stomach, the doctor exhausts his experience in vain. The very centre of recovery is attacked, and science can offer little or no help. In the same way, if a nation's sentiment has been depraved, every absurdity finds credence, and every crime finds a defender. Religion, legislation, morality, rights, everything is in chaos.

All institutions should tend solely to purify the sentiment of conscience from every foreign taint, and this sentiment will then be able to lead man to virtue and happiness. No code of morality, no Catechism of Probity – these are not words you should teach the people. Instead you should prevent natural sentiment from being corrupted.

Above all, you must not profit from the weakness of man's brain to transform it from his birth by the two methods of fright and wonder. You will stifle the inner voice, you will shatter sentiment, and crime will inundate the earth as the ocean would flood Holland if a clumsy or a criminal hand should break the dykes, fruits of the centuries and of experience.

The lawgiver, after having assured everyone some portion of property by civil law, should then assure them, through criminal law, of their life and the maintenance of their liberty, and should assure them through his political law of the integrity of their rights and of their dignity. In his paternal solicitude, he should sweep away anything which might tend to lead them astray. Imposture and adroitly presented fairy stories should no longer surround the cradle. Above all this perfidious music should be prohibited. Let those who infringe these two laws of protection and conservation be punished as poisoners of the public.

You have told man to return to himself, you have restored him to nature, whose all-powerful voice will lead him to happiness. These, gentlemen, are the sentiments that one should inculcate in men for their happiness.

PART THREE

. . . A corrupted people has its natural sentiments perverted by need, unease or the frenzy of a violent imagination. Often, superstition is their sickness. Enthusiasm is a violent emotion in some people. Enthusiasm is the delirium of reason, as superstition is the depravation of sentiment.

One must therefore start by establishing natural sentiment, because if it is perverted, reason becomes a false guide. But what am I saying? Reason! It no longer exists. It is transformed, prejudice and sophism replace it, and man strays, never to return.

With natural sentiment and balanced logic, chaste and pure reason springs from the brain of man as once Minerva did from that of the Father of the Gods . . . If we assume natural sentiment in all its force, all you need to do is to assist the development of logic, all you need to do is to fortify it so that it cannot delude man and lead him astray in his calculations. As an indispensable preliminary you must wipe out all the confusion of argument, and let nothing remain but the advance of analysis.

To develop and fortify logic, you should act as if you were teaching a child to walk; show him a science where everything is resolved by logic, where all is logic : the mathematical science. There is no better course in logic.

Should the people learn mathematics, then? Would this be so absurd? Do you not make them learn their catechism? Well then, if instead you substituted a short course in geometry would that be impracticable or less useful? I would like to see young people who were being taught a few of Euclid's propositions. Their logic would find a firm grounding, and so would their reason. But I have not said, I do not claim that one should transform the shepherds' or labourers' huts into schools. I do not think that science is indispensable to man, and certainly I do not think that without Euclid man cannot be happy. The labourer must teach his art to his son. The art of labour consists of many facts and a few reasonings. That is a mathematical science. Every useful art offers as much, and every artisan learns a mathematical science in his apprenticeship.

As for the class that is especially destined to govern or guide the others along the path of truth, it must cultivate the art of logic more closely. A good course in geometry and algebra will fulfil this goal perfectly. History, the basis of moral sciences, the torch of truth, the destroyer of prejudices should not be forgotten either. With these two sciences, every political truth will be revealed before their eyes. They will be in a position to render powerful assistance to public prosperity.

Work in the fields or in the workshop calms the fevered imagination. The worker in the field does not know that anxiety which devours the indolent. Though his reason may be scarcely formed, it is sufficient to guide him, to temper the impulsiveness of his sentiment, or to contain the starts of his imagination. He, on the other hand, who strays in his indolence, must have a better framed and more powerful reason. The torrent is stronger, the dykes must be so too . . . Observation is more necessary to him, he needs all the energy of reason. Does he feel the fire of genius circulating in his veins? Wretched man, I am sorry for him. He will be the admiration and envy of his fellow men and the most miserable of all. His equilibrium is upset; he will be unhappy . . . Ah! the fire of genius! . . . but let us not alarm ourselves, it is so rare. How many years pass without nature producing one. Men of genius are meteors destined to blaze in order to light up their century.

Since man can only taste happiness in a life which conforms to his organisation; since, because of his intellectual organisation, reason is the guiding light of his actions, since constraint depraves and annihilates him, one must never force anyone to adopt views which he does not feel.

Entire and absolute freedom of thought, freedom of speech and writing in anything which does not harm the social order, that must be the foundation of morality, liberty and individual happiness. Natural rights must therefore only be limited by a precise law, and this law cannot prohibit actions other than those directly contrary to society. If it were otherwise the social order would be a calamity, an intolerable slavery.

Reason yields a part of her rights that she can only keep with her independence, but she yields this part to the general reason. The law must be an expression of this, and can therefore only concern general objectives. It is an acquiescence of individual reason in the general reason, on those objectives which interest all citizens.

Without liberty, nations can possess no energy, virtue or strength. Without energy, virtue or strength there can be no sentiment or natural reason, there can be no happiness.

. . . These principles should be constantly repeated to mankind; resisting oppression is man's finest right, the one of which the tyrants are most afraid. They have been alarmed by it in every age. They would have succeeded in completely effacing it were it not inherent in man's nature, and if the Creator had not, through sentiment, engraved it in eternal characters: after centuries, Frenchmen, brutalised by kings and their ministers, nobles and their prejudices, priests and their impostures, suddenly awoke and mapped out the rights of mankind. May they serve as a guide to lawgivers. Then we will see less wicked people, because they will be happy. The influence of good laws on morality and on individual passions is incalculable, and morality and the modification of passion determine happiness.

If there is a political constitution and a political liberty, there is also an animal constitution and an animal liberty, there is also a moral constitution and a moral liberty.

Through the animal constitution, hands touch, eyes see, feet walk, and the mouth speaks.

Through the moral constitution, sentiment enjoys all the development to which it is susceptible. Man identifies himself with his wife, sees himself in his children, opens his heart in friendship, rejoices in nature, shares the way of life of his region, and the happiness of his people. Through the moral constitution, reason modifies the heat of sentiment, and ensures its prolongation, enlightens and contains the imagination and dictates man's external conduct. Through the moral constitution he is perfected, he rejoices in perfection. He gives advice, he foresees, he rejoices in his own utility, and his foresight. These are the laws of the human constitution or organisation. If one obeys them one lives happily.

What is political liberty? It is nothing but obeying the laws of the political constitution.

What is animal liberty? It is nothing but obeying the laws of the animal constitution.

What is moral liberty? It is nothing but obeying the laws of the moral constitution.

Everything which moves us strongly unsettles the nerves and the stomach, exhausts the blood . . . Chastity and libertinism, fasting and debauchery, complete repose and excessive fatigue, the labour of the academic and of the warrior are equally unnatural, equally destructive of our constitution, and hence of animal liberty.

As for moral liberty, it has basically two principal enemies: bad political laws and domination by the strong and the usurper. We have already discussed this and concluded that nature abhors death less than slavery, because slavery is the dissolution worse, the suffering of the spirit, while death transfigures it.

The second enemy of moral liberty and hence of man's happiness will not leave him until it has subjugated him. It crosses the sea and climbs the rocks with him. In the heart of the town, or the country, to whichever corner of the earth he may go, the violent passion which has mastered him follows him still.

Whether ambition, greed for riches, love or any other passion possesses man, it deals the death blow to repose, and at least for a time to happiness.

Violent passion upsets the economy of the animal constitution. All the organs are disturbed in their function. They are in anarchy. From this point of view, such passion is destructive of animal liberty.

Violent passion annihilates the subtle and sublime sentiment of existence, friendship, gratitude and tender respect. Nature no longer has any charms. The thick scum of effervescence veils nature from man's eyes. Violent passion wants what it wants. It allows no contrast, reason disappears, prejudice arrives and man is abandoned defenceless to it. But violent passion is not content. It calls in to its aid the unbridled imagination, which is proud and joyous in the humiliation of its enemy reason, and comes to possess its victim in order to torment him with every type of evil.

Happiness is therefore incompatible with violent passion, since passion is destructive of the animal economy, sentiment and natural reason.

Behold this young adolescent, abandoned to love. He is agitated, he groans, he weeps, a devouring fire circulates in his veins. Nothing can calm him. What does he want? What is wrong with him? What does he desire? Sometimes he trembles, he bellows like the African lion. Sometimes he sings with the melody of the swan or the tenderness of the turtledove. He creates monsters in his mind in order to fight them and be tormented by them. The world is reduced for him to a single room, opinion to a single voice, happiness to one fantasy. Morality, virtue, society, nature, his country, a father and mother cherished up until now, everything becomes foreign to him, everything becomes insupportable, because there can be no morality, no virtue, no society, no parents without duties to perform. And he does not fulfil his duties. He respects none but those of his passion. Doubtless he feels pleasures and pains, but do they compensate for each other? . . . But that is not the question we are discussing. Is he blessed with natural sentiment? No. Is he blessed with reason? All he knows is the prejudice of passion, and this being so, even if he could accumulate every imaginable pleasure, he would not be living in conformity with his organisation. He does not enjoy either animal or moral liberty.

His adolescence is over. This same young man has attained the virile age, and ambition has mastered him . . . Ambition with its pale complexion, its wandering eyes, its precipitous gait, its irregular movements, and its sardonic laugh. Crimes are no more than games to him. The cabal is nothing but a means. Deceit, calumny, and slander are nothing but the tricks of rhetoric and argument. When he eventually arrives at the helm of affairs, the homage of the people fatigues him. But he can do good. Is there anything more consoling to reason than to be able to say: "I have just ensured the happiness of a hundred families. I have expended my energy over this, but the state will be better for it. The lives of my fellow citizens are calm through my anxiety, happy through my perplexity, gay through my vexations." Yes, but you have not noticed that that is how Fabricius and Cincinnatus reasoned, and Fabricius and Cincinnatus were not ambitious. That man who desires to make his way solely because he is impelled by the pure sentiment of contributing to public felicity is a virtuous man, who knows his own courage, firmness, and talents. He will master ambition, instead of being mastered by it, and he will therefore be able to enjoy sentiment and reason. He will always rejoice in moral liberty.

. . . When I attempted to set my course through a sea famed for its shipwrecks, I only considered the utility of the voyage. Have I had no greater fortune? Have I failed to reach my goal?

I am not surprised. In pursuing my course, I have only encountered people who have lost their way. Have I imitated
them? I am sure at least that someone will have succeeded and
I am consoled in that my struggles will increase the triumph
of the victor, certain that mediocrity will not carry off the prize,
since with your reputation, you will discuss it heatedly.

A Madrigal *(1792)*

Dedicated to Madame Saint-Huberty, on the occasion of her triumph in Piccini's opera Dido. *She was singing the title role.*

Romans, who boast of your origin bright,
See from what chance a great Empire may flower;
Dido's attraction held too little power
To keep back her obstinate lover from flight.

But if our own Dido, of these lands the pride,
Had been queen of Carthage;
To serve her, he'd gladly his gods have denied –
Your beautiful land to this day would be savage.

PART FOUR

Napoleon Supports the Mountain

June to August, 1793

The Bonaparte family arrived in Toulon on June 13 1793. Napoleon had given up all hope of making a successful career in Corsica, and of working with Paoli. His first task was to ensure the safety of his mother, brothers and sisters. He tried to settle them in various different villages and towns including Bausset, Mionnac and, eventually, Marseilles. Napoleon was able to contact Jean DuTeil (brother of his former artillery instructor), and was assigned the task of helping to co-ordinate coastal defences. This earned him some money, and kept his family from abject poverty. But the Midi was in a state of civil war. After the fall of the Girondins at the beginning of June, a departmental congress held at Lyon had denied the legality of the new Jacobin government, the "Mountain". Toulon and Marseilles had also risen in protest. Napoleon was ordered to report for duty with General Carteaux' army, stationed at Pontet, seven miles from Avignon. The Marseillais had taken Avignon, and Carteaux was about to advance against them. A popular tradition states that Napoleon's guns destroyed the Marseillais gun-emplacements in the ensuing action. In fact, he probably took no part in the actual attack: his brief was simply to organise the artillery for Carteaux' force. After the siege of Avignon Napoleon stayed in Beaucaire to recover from a short illness, and may have based his political pamphlet Supper in Beaucaire *on an actual dinner-table discussion. This polemic was written to persuade the people of Marseilles to submit to the "Mountain", in the interest of republican unity. Although Napoleon shows some sympathy for the moderate republicanism of the Marseillais in the discussion he writes as a convinced Jacobin.*

Introduction

WE HAVE seen how Napoleon, while he was on garrison duty at Auxonne, Valence and Douai, was leading a double life, and writing in two distinct styles. He seldom wrote creatively when he was actually in Corsica, during his extended periods of leave in 1786, 1788 and 1789, but he did gather material for his projected history of the island – mainly from unpublished manuscripts in Bastia, and from heated discussions in Ajaccio cafés. He wrote a sycophantic letter to Paoli from Auxonne, trying to interest the veteran revolutionary in his project. Napoleon describes his feelings on returning to his native land after nine years in the *Discours de Lyon*. During his third leave in September 1789 to February 1791, the political situation had changed radically. France was free, but Corsica was still oppressed: this time, he combined his studies with committed political agitation. He sent a part of the *History of Corsica*, written in the form of a letter, to the Abbé Raynal; at the same time he encouraged the citizens of Ajaccio to open a club, the "Globo Patriotico", persuaded it to draft a petition to the National Assembly, and whipped up a riot in Bastia to support the petition. He also arranged for his brother Joseph, who was not of the legal age, to help in the regional assemblies. His brother Lucien describes Napoleon's dual occupations at this time. "He helped in the Société Populaire . . . at the same time he did me the honour of reading me his political, and even poetic compositions that he had engaged me to re-copy : I did this with pleasure".

Bonaparte was still working hard on his *History*, constantly revising it, and waiting for Paoli to return from a twenty-year exile in London : together they could lead Corsica into action. But Napoleon over-played his hand : he antagonised Paoli at their first meeting on the old battlefield of Pont Nuovo, the scene of Paoli's decisive defeat by French troops in 1769. Symbolically, the argument started when Napoleon applied the theoretical maxims he had learned at Auxonne to Paoli's nostal-

113

gic description of how his troops had been deployed, and tact-
lessly suggested that "with those dispositions, the outcome of
the battle was inevitable". Bonaparte tried to win the old man's
support by defending him in the *Letter to Buttafuoco,* but
Paoli was unimpressed. On March 16 1791, Paoli was asked
by Napoleon to send some unpublished material for use in the
history: he replied that young men could not possibly write
presentable history. As a result, the third letter on Corsica was
never completed. (See Masson and Biagi, *Napoléon Inconnu.*)

It was during his stay in Corsica early in 1791 that Napoleon
had conceived the idea of entering the Lyon Essay Competition,
to establish some reputation in *French* literary circles. Napoleon's
interest in Corsica seems to have become more actively political
at this time. He continued to study the military potential of
Corsica, and amass statistics on the strategic strength of Ajaccio,
but this was in case it should ever be necessary to protect Corsica
against England. It was not until June 1793 that Napoleon gave
up all hope of working with Paoli, and decided to channel his
energies into a career in France – a career which he had left
open for just this eventuality. In future, he wrote about Corsica
with detachment, and even cynicism. As early as December
1791, Napoleon abruptly stopped taking notes on other literary works and writing short stories or philosophical discourses:
apart from his correspondence and one poem, all his writings
from January 1792 to July 1793 concern military or political
activity – rules for the voluntary national guard, justificatory
pieces about the Sardinia expedition, and about the riots of
April 1792, projects for the defence of Ajaccio etc. Up to 1791,
most of Napoleon's professional military writings had simply
been concerned with his garrison duties – memoranda on artillery tests. By 1792, he claimed to be working towards a "simple
and concise" style for more creative writings about military and
political matters. For the first time, only a military tactician
could understand these highly specialised works. Napoleon's
letter to Matteo Buttafuoco was a specific attack on the Corsican
deputy at the National Assembly. The pamphlet is clumsy, since
Napoleon was incapable of writing wih irony about political
figures, but the Ajaccio club voted to print the work. Napoleon
could not afford to be too excited by the prospect of appearing

in print; he wanted to wait for Paoli's verdict on the the pamphlet. When it came, Paoli's judgement was brief and to the point : "It would have made a greater impression if it had tried to say less". Napoleon made a final attempt to please Paoli in his *Address to the Convention* of April 1793, in which he complained of the Convention's suspicions about the Generalissimo, but in the same month he wrote a *Petition to the municipality of Ajaccio* asking the citizens to take the oath to the French Republic. Despite the fact that both works were written to be read out, the style is controlled and even. By the first of June 1793, when Napoleon wrote the *Memoir on the political and military position of the Department of Corsica,* he had made his decision : the pamphlet violently attacks Paoli and his partisans for their attitude to the French Revolution, and for their insistence on selling themselves to the English. There are no extended metaphors, rhetorical digressions or clumsy attempts at moralising : it is a pamphlet written by a man of action. This format is repeated in Napoleon's famous pamphlet *Supper in Beaucaire,* written in July 1793.

*

Napoleon, by now a senior captain in the first Regiment of Artillery, was stationed in Nice from June 1793. At the beginning of July, he received a mission from General DuTeil, the younger brother of his former commandant at Auxonne : Napoleon had to go to Avignon to organise the powder convoys which were to be sent on to the army in Italy, and to help co-ordinate the coastal defence batteries of the Mediterranean section. On July 15th, Napoleon was transferred to General Carteaux' army, where he was to organise the artillery in the forthcoming attack on the rebels in Avignon.

The Confederated section of the Midi had risen in protest after the fall of the Girondins. The Marseillais had occupied Avignon, an important ammunition centre for the army in Italy. A small force, led by General Carteaux, was marching to dislodge them, via Pont Saint Esprit and Orange. A popular tradition, which was started by Avignonnais historians, states that Napoleon took part in Carteaux' attack on Avignon, and that, with only two cannon – strategically placed on the Ville-neuve heights – he destroyed the Marseillais gun-emplacements. There is no evidence for this mythical version of the facts from Carteaux, Albitte, Dommartin, or indeed from Napoleon him-self, to substantiate the story. In *Supper in Beaucaire,* there is no allusion to the rôle he played at Avignon; he was simply in the region at the time, and in charge of the artillery attached to the attacking force. (See Chuquet, op. cit.)

Carteaux' version states the following : General Carteaux attacked Avignon from four sides on July 24/25 : but the town was well fortified, and he considered his four pounders could not give him enough battery support to break through their defences. At 10 o'clock at night, the troops returned to camp. At 4 o'clock the following afternoon, a deputation from Avignon announced that the gates were open, and that the Marseillais had fled in disorder. At 9 o'clock in the evening, Carteaux marched into Avignon amid public acclamations.

Napoleon's version is contained in *Supper in Beaucaire.* Although he was probably nowhere near the Avignon action on July 25, he must have known some of the facts to write the one-sided description the pamphlet contains. Carteaux, apparently made no "formal attack" – he was simply skirmishing to try the strength of the garrison. Carteaux' control of com-munications in the region was a decisive factor in causing the Marseillais to lose their nerve. Napoleon had made an effort to find out about the "guerre du Midi" : he knew of the incident at Lisle and of the cavalry's attack on the Marseillais as they retreated. But he made two mistakes, both of which show that he took no part in the attack on Avignon. First, he says that Dubois-Crancé was one of the representatives who followed Carteaux' army into Avignon. In fact, Dubois-Crancé was in Grenoble at the time. Secondly, he writes that the Allobroges were in Villeneuve : in fact, Villeneuve was occupied by adjutant-general Dours' column, and there were no Allobroges in his ranks. The Allobroges were encamped at Pontet, twenty of their dragoons were in the vanguard which entered Avignon on July 25, 100 others joined them later and, without any artillery of their own, took two cannon from the retreating Mar-seillais : Napoleon would certainly have mentioned these facts if he had known of them. His omissions and mistakes seem to be more than just the results of over-hasty writing.

While Carteaux' army marched on to Marseilles, and scoured the region for breakaway units, Napoleon almost certainly continued to organise his powder convoys at Avignon, drawing up lengthy inventories, and arranging gun-emplacements which would probably never be used. On August 25 he wrote to Paris asking to be posted elsewhere : he wanted to see some action, and requested a lieutenant-colonelship in the army of the Rhine. His request was refused by the Jacobin Minister of War.

*

In July 1793, Napoleon addressed his pamphlet *Supper in Beaucaire* to the Representatives of the Convention, who agreed to pay for it to be printed. Basically it is written to show the strength of Carteaux' army, and the foolishness of the Marseilles rebels in trying to oppose Republican forces. To make his argument more readable, Napoleon wrote the pamphlet as a "conversation" between a soldier who represents the Jacobin point of view, two defenders of the Marseillais cause, and two civilians from the region who are the supposedly impartial contributors to the discussion : their function is to channel the conversation in the right direction, and encourage the Marseillais to reach a Republican conclusion. The Montpellier manufacturer speaks only twice, the man from Nîmes three times; of the two Marseillais, only one takes part in the discussion, so that effectively *Supper in Beaucaire* is another of Napoleon's dialogues in the Socratic mould.

In the *Dialogue on Love*, Napoleon was treating a philosophical subject in semi-abstract terms, and maintaining the readers' interest by suggesting the clash of two very different personalities : here, he is describing a recent event in terms which are calculated to convince the rebels to lay down their arms. The soldier's speeches are brisk and single-minded; when he has to explain a question of detail Napoleon writes in more complex sentences, but never loses control of his material. Questions are asked by the civilians, the soldier replies with precision, the Marseillais deny the facts vehemently, and the soldier calmly refutes them. Inevitably, the Marseillais are eventually convinced, and they buy several bottles of champagne for the assembled company, to show that there are no hard feelings. The discussion is not completely one-sided : the Marseillais makes some strong points about the Girondin leaders and about the conditions on which he would accept the constitution (from a representative he can esteem). And Napoleon cannot afford to be too strongly in favour of Carteaux and Albitte : he praises the patriotic traditions of the Marseilles region, and is cautious when describing the Brissotins.

But in the end, Napoleon's defence of the Mountain – even of its excesses – convinces everyone because of its basic pragmatism : the Mountain must be obeyed because it is successful, and because it must be victorious. As Napoleon said in his mémoire of June 1793 on the *Department of Corsica* : "If one must belong to a party, it must be that which triumphs; it is better to be the eater than the eaten". *Supper in Beaucaire* contains no illusions about this philosophy. As the soldier says, four years of troubles have perfected man's natural discernment.

The vocabulary of the pamphlet is interesting. The military axioms and details of artillery warfare are expressed as considered, professional opinions : they are not too specialised, but they do reflect Napoleon's long training in Auxonne and Valence. Napoleon also uses the fashionable republican jargon of 1793 – for example, "faire danser la carmagnole à l'ennemi". By 1799, this ability to adapt to French styles and phrases will have become second nature to Napoleon. His *Discourse to the Council of the Ancients,* delivered on November 10 1799 contains individual words, phrases, even sentences which strikingly reflect Danton's inflammatory speech to the National Convention of March 1793. Napoleon's variations on French Revolutionary oratory, are, however, concise rather than hysterical : the influences of his youth – Rousseau, Raynal, Paoli and Charles Bonaparte – no longer have a place in his style.

Supper in Beaucaire

OR

a Discussion between a Soldier of Carteaux's army, a Marseillais, a Man from Nimes, and a Manufacturer from Montpellier, on the Events which have Occurred in the Former County, on the Arrival of the Men from Marseilles.

I FOUND MYSELF in Beaucaire on the last day of the fair. As luck would have it, I had as table companions for supper two Marseilles merchants, a man from Nîmes and a manufacturer from Montpellier. After a few moments spent in getting acquainted, they had found out that I had come from Avignon, and that I was a soldier. The minds of my table-companions which all week had been fixed on the progress of trade as a means of making money, were at this moment fixed on the outcome of current events, on which the future of their livelihood depended. They wanted to find out my opinion, so that in comparing it with their own, they might adjust their views and assess prospects for a future which would affect us all differently.

The Marseillais seemed to be particularly depressed. The evacuation of Avignon had taught them to have doubts about everything – all they had left was a considerable anxiety about their fate. Mutual confidence soon made us talkative and we embarked on a conversation more or less on these lines.

THE MAN FROM NIMES

Is Carteaux' army strong? They say it has lost many men in the attack, but if it is true that the army has suffered a setback, then why have the Marseillais evacuated Avignon?

119

THE SOLDIER

The army was four thousand strong when it attacked Avignon. Today there are six thousand men, and before four days are out there will be ten thousand. Carteaux has lost five dead, with four wounded. He certainly did not suffer a set-back, since he made no formal attack.

The army skirmished around the town, tried to force the gates by planting explosives and fired a few cannon to test the garrison's resistance. Soon after, they had to withdraw to camp, in order to plan the attack for the following night. The Marseillais numbered three thousand six hundred men. They had more artillery and of superior calibre; in spite of this they were forced to retreat across the Durance. That astonishes you: but the reason is that only veteran troops can stand up to the uncertainties of a siege. We were in control of the Rhone, Villeneuve and the countryside: we would have cut all lines of communication. They had to evacuate the town. The cavalry pursued them as they retreated. Many of their men were captured and they lost two cannon.

THE MARSEILLAIS

That is not the version we have been given. I do not want to argue with you, since you were actually there; but you must admit that all this will lead you nowhere.

Our army is at Aix; three good generals have arrived to replace the original ones. We are recruiting fresh battalions in Marseilles, we have got a new artillery train, with several twenty-four pounders. In a very few days, we will be ready to re-take Avignon, or at least we will retain control of the Durance.

SOLDIER

That is what they tell you to lure you into the chasm which deepens with every instant, and which will, perhaps, engulf the finest town in France; a town which has well deserved its share of patriots. But they also told you that you would march across France, that you would set the proper tone for the Republic – and your first steps have only been set-backs. You were told that Avignon could long resist twenty thousand men, yet a single column of the army, without siege artillery, took the town in twenty-four hours : they told you that the Midi was up in arms, but you found yourselves alone. They told you that the cavalry from Nîmes would destroy the Allobroges – yet the Allobroges were already in St Esprit and Villeneuve. They told you that four thousand Lyonnais were marching to relieve you – but the Lyonnais were negotiating terms.

Accept the fact that they are misleading you, realise that your leaders are incompetent, and beware of their predictions. Self-esteem is the most dangerous of counsellors. You are naturally impetuous, you are being led to the slaughter by the same means that have destroyed so many peoples . . . by exciting your vanity. You are a wealthy people, and your population is considerable – but your leaders are exaggerating these facts. You have done splendid service for liberty – they remind you of this, without noting the fact that the guiding spirit of the Republic was with you then, whereas today it forsakes you.

You tell me that your army is at Aix with a great artillery train and good generals; well, whatever your army does, I assure you it will be defeated.

You had three thousand six hundred men – at least half of them have scattered; Marseilles plus a few refugees of the department might be able to offer you four thousand men; that is a great deal . . . So you will then have five to six thousand men, with no co-ordination, no unity and no experience of battle. You have good generals . . . I have yet to see them so I cannot comment on their talents, but they will be bogged down in details and will not be supported by subalterns; they will be able to achieve nothing to sustain any reputation they may have acquired, for it will take them two months to organise their army even tolerably well, and in four days Carteaux will have crossed the Durance, and with real soldiers.

With the excellent light troops of the Allobroges, the experienced Bourgogne regiment, a good cavalry regiment, the gallant battalion of the Côte d'Or which has seen victory march a hundred times before it into battle, and six or seven other forces, all veteran militia-men whose inspiration comes from their successes on the frontiers and against your army. You have some eighteen and twenty-four pounders and you think yourselves undefeatable – you are following vulgar opinion, but the professionals will tell you, and inevitable experience will make it quite clear that good four and eight pounders have as much effect in open warfare, and are superior in many ways.

Your gunners are raw recruits; your opposite numbers are artillery men of the line, whose skill makes them masters of Europe. What will become of your army if it concentrates on Aix? The army will be lost – it is a precept of military science that he who entrenches his position is sure to be defeated. Theory and practice agree on this point, and the city-walls of Aix are not as good as the worst entrenchments in open country, particularly if you consider the area they cover, and the houses which surround them within pistol-range. You can be quite certain, then, that the choice which seems the best to you, is in fact the worst. Besides, how will you manage to furnish the town in so little time with all the supplies it will need? Will your army actually go out and look for the enemy? It has less men, its artillery is less suitable for open country – it will be harassed, then completely destroyed, for the cavalry will prevent it from re-grouping.

Then you can expect war in the region of Marseilles itself : a sufficiently numerous party there stands up for the Republic; that will be the moment for them to act . . . they will effect a link-up of forces and this town, the centre of Levantine commerce, the main market of Southern Europe, will be lost . . . Remember the recent example of Lisle and the inhuman laws of war !

But what kind of dizziness can suddenly have possessed your people? What fatal blindness leads you to the slaughter? How can you possibly aspire to resist the entire Republic? Even if you force the Republic's army to fall back on Avignon can you doubt that in a very few days fresh forces will come to replace

it. Will the Republic, which makes the law for the whole of
Europe, take it from Marseilles?

In collaboration with Bordeaux, Lyon, Montpellier, Nîmes,
Grenoble, the Jura, the Eure and the Calvados, you embarked
on a revolution. You had some chance of success – your ringleaders may have had dubious motives but you had an imposing
show of force; on the other hand, now that Lyon, Nîmes, Montpellier, Bordeaux, the Jura and Eure, Grenoble and Caen have
accepted the Constitution, now that Avignon, Tarascon and
Arles have yielded, you must admit that your stubbornness is
rather foolish. You are influenced by people who, having nothing to lose, involve you in their downfall. Your army will have
to be composed of all the most well-to-do, the wealthiest of
your town, for the sans-culottes could too easily turn against
you. So you will be endangering the cream of your youth –
accustomed to maintaining the commercial balance of the
Mediterranean, and to enriching you by their good manage-
ment and their speculations – against experienced soldiers a
hundred times stained with the blood of the frenzied aristocrat
or the ferocious Prussian.

Let poorer regions fight to the last ditch; the inhabitant of
the Vivarais, of the Cevennes, and of Corsica will expose himself
fearlessly to the outcome of battle; if he wins, he has achieved
his goal, if he loses he finds himself in the position to make peace
in exactly the same circumstances as before.

. . . But you! ! . . . you lose one battle and the fruit of a
thousand years of hard work, exertion, thrift and happiness
becomes the soldier's prey. Yet these are the risks that they, so
thoughtlessly, make you run.

THE MARSEILLAIS

You are going too fast, and you alarm me; I agree with you
that the situation is critical; perhaps you are right that we
have not thought deeply enough about the position we find
ourselves in; but you must admit that we still have vast resources
with which to oppose you. You have convinced me that we
would not be able to hold out in Aix; your comments on our

lack of provisions for a long siege are perhaps undeniable; but do you think that all Provence will coolly stand by and watch the blockade of Aix?

The whole region will rise of its own accord, and your army, hemmed in on all sides, will be lucky to re-cross the Durance.

THE SOLDIER

How little you know of men's minds and of the mood of the present time! Wherever there is a division into two sides, the moment you are besieged, the breakaway party will get the worst of every open confrontation; the examples of Tarascon, Orgon and Arles must convince you of that; twenty dragoons were enough to re-establish the original administrators and make the others flee in disorder.

From now on, any major uprising in your favour is out of the question in your department – it could have taken place when your enemy had not crossed the Durance and when your forces were undivided; in Toulon, opinions differ a great deal and the breakaway party do not hold the same sway there as in Marseilles: they must therefore remain within their town to control their adversaries . . . As for the Basses Alpes, you know that practically the whole Department has accepted the Constitution.

THE MARSEILLAIS

We will attack Carteaux in our mountains where his cavalry will be of no use to him.

THE SOLDIER

As if an army which is defending a town could dictate the choice of battlefield. In any case it is false to suppose that there is any terrain in this region mountainous enough to nullify the effect of cavalry; however, your hills are steep enough to make the artillery's task more difficult and so give a great advantage to your enemies. For it is in broken-up terrain that a good gunner can show his superior mobility, training and judgement of distances.

THE MARSEILLAIS

So you think we are without any resources? Can it possibly be the fate of this town which resisted the Romans and maintained some of its own laws under the despots who followed them, to become booty for a few brigands? What! Shall the Allobroges, laden with the spoils of Lisle, lay down the law in Marseilles! What! Shall Dubois-Crancé and Albitte go unopposed? Shall these blood-stained men that regrettable circumstance has placed at the helm of political affairs become absolute masters? What a gloomy prospect you offer me. Our property would be usurped on various pretexts. We would be the constant victims of those soldiers that muster under the same colours only for the sake of pillage. Our worthiest citizens would be imprisoned and would perish unjustly. The Club would once again raise its ugly head to execute its hellish schemes. Nothing could be worse than this horrible idea; it would be better to risk oneself in the hope of winning than to be a victim without the option.

THE SOLDIER

That is civil war; people cut each other to pieces, detest each other and kill other people they know nothing about . . . Who do you think the Allobroges are? Africans? Inhabitants of Siberia? Eh! Nothing of the kind . . . they are your fellow-countrymen, people from Provence, from Dauphiny, from Savoy. You think them barbarians because their name is foreign. If your forces were called "the Phocæan Phalanx" all sorts of legends would be held against them for that reason alone. I must admit you have reminded me of one fact, namely the incident at Lisle; I am not going to justify it, but I will explain it. The defenders of Lisle killed the herald that we sent them; they resisted without hope of success, they were taken by storm; the soldiers entered the town in the midst of the chaos of fire and death, it was no longer possible to control them; indignation did the rest. These soldiers whom you call brigands are our best troops and our most disciplined battalions – their reputation is above scandal. Dubois-Crancé and Albitte are steadfast friends of the people, they have never swerved from the straight course . . . they are scoundrels only in the eyes of rogues. But Condorcet, Brissot and Barbaroux were also called scoundrels when their actions were in fact unimpeachable; to be considered infamous by the vicious will always be the prerogative of the virtuous. You seem to think that they go to extremes with you; on the contrary, they are treating you like misguided children . . . do you think that Marseilles could have withdrawn the merchandise she had in Beaucaire without their consent? They could have sequestered the merchandise right from the start of the war. They did not wish to do that and thanks to them, you can go home in peace.

You call Carteaux an assassin: well! you should know that this general is extremely anxious to maintain order and discipline; witness his conduct at St. Esprit and Avignon. Not a pin was taken. He had a sergeant imprisoned – who had presumed to arrest a Marseillais of your army who had stayed behind in a house – for invading a citizen's privacy without an express order. Some men from Avignon were punished for presuming to describe a house as "aristocratic". A soldier was sent for trial because he had been accused of theft . . .

Your army, on the other hand, has killed, assassinated more than thirty people, invaded family privacy and filled the prisons with good citizens under the vague pretext that they were brigands.

You need not be afraid of the army; it holds Marseilles in esteem because it knows that no other town has made so many sacrifices to the public good. You have eighteen thousand men at the frontier and you have not spared yourselves, regardless of the situation. Shake off the yoke of those few aristocrats who lead you, return to saner principles and you will have no truer friend than the soldier.

THE MARSEILLAIS

Ah! your soldiers have certainly degenerated since the army of 1789; that army had no desire to take up arms against the nation; your soldiers ought to imitate such a fine example and refrain from turning their arms against good citizens.

THE SOLDIER

If we had followed this principle, the Vendée would today be flying the white flag on the walls of the restored Bastille, and the Jalès faction would be lording it over Marseilles!

THE MARSEILLAIS

The Vendée wants a king; the Vendée wants open counter-revolution. The struggle of the Vendée and of the Jalès faction is a struggle for fanaticism and despotism; ours on the other hand is that of true Republicans, friends of law and order, enemies of anarchy and the wicked. Do we not fly the tricolour flag? And what interest would we have in wanting slavery?

THE SOLDIER

I am well aware that the people of Marseilles is far removed from the people of the Vendée as far as counter-revolution goes. The people of the Vendée are strong and healthy; those of Marseilles weak and sickly, they need to have the pill sweetened; to establish the new doctrine, they have to be fed lies. But during four years of revolution, after so many cabals, plots and conspiracies, the whole range of human perversity has developed, man's natural discernment has evolved; this is so true that, in spite of the departmental coalition, in spite of the skill of the leaders, the vast amount of resources at their disposal and the union of all the enemies of the Revolution, the people everywhere has woken up just when they were thought to be under the evil spell.

You say that you fly the tricolour flag . . .

Paoli also hoisted that flag, in Corsica, to give himself time to deceive the people, to crush the true friends of liberty, in order to lure his fellow-countrymen into his ambitious and criminal schemes. He hoisted the tricolour flag; and he opened fire on ships belonging to the Republic; and he drove our troops from their fortresses; and he disarmed those who guarded them; and he organised riots in order to harass those Republicans who remained on the Island, and he pillaged the storehouses, selling everything in them at giveaway prices in order to have money to sustain his revolt. He plundered and confiscated the belongings of the most well-to-do families because they supported the unity of the Republic; and he declared "enemies of the fatherland" all those who stayed in our armies. Before that, he had caused the failure of the expedition against Sardinia. And still he was shameless enough to call himself friend of France, and a good Republican; and still he deceived the Convention which repealed the order for his discharge.

He managed things so well in the end, that when he had been unmasked by his own letters found at Calvi, it was already too late; enemy fleets were intercepting all communications.

We should no longer put our trust in words. We must analyse deeds, and you must admit that looking at yours, it is easy to show you to be counter-revolutionaries.

What effect has your movement produced on the Republic? You have led it almost to ruin, you have hampered our army operations. I do not know if you have been in the pay of the Spaniard and the Austrian, but they certainly could not have wished for a happier diversion. What more could you do if you were in their pay? Every well-known aristocrat is anxious for your success. You have put avowed aristocrats at the head of your administration and your armies; someone called Latourette, a colonel before the Revolution, a certain Somise, a lieutenant-colonel of the Engineers before the Revolution, both of whom abandoned their troops at the outbreak of war so as not to have to fight for the liberty of the people. Your battalions are full of such people and your cause would not be theirs if it was that of the Republic.

THE MARSEILLAIS

But are Brissot, Barbaroux, Condorcet, Verniaud, Guadet etc. also aristocrats? Who founded the Republic? Who overthrew the tyrant, who in the last resort sustained our mother country through the perilous times of the last campaign?

THE SOLDIER

I am not trying to find out if these men who so often have

served the people well, have ever conspired against them. It is enough for me to know that after the Mountain, by public and party spirit, had proceeded as far as possible against them, issued writs and imprisoned them, I will even admit had slandered them, the Brissotins would have been finished without a civil war which put them in a position to dictate to their enemies.

So your war was really useful to them. If they had deserved their initial reputation, they would have thrown down their arms at the sight of the Constitution, they would have sacrificed their interest to the public good; but it is far easier to quote Decius than to imitate him. Today, they stand guilty of the most heinous of all crimes. They have justified the decrees against them by their conduct . . . the blood they have spilled has washed away any real services they may have performed in the past.

THE MANUFACTURER FROM MONTPELLIER

Your view of the question is the one most favourable to these gentlemen; for it seems proven that the Brissotins were really guilty. But, guilty or not, we no longer live in a century when people fight over personalities.

England has shed torrents of blood over the houses of York and Lancaster, France over the Lorraines and the Bourbons. Are we still living in those barbarous times?

THE MAN FROM NIMES

Precisely. That is why we abandoned the Marseillais the moment we saw that they sought counter-revolution, and that they were fighting over personal grievances. The mask fell as soon as they refused to promulgate the Constitution. That is why we forgave the Mountain a few irregularities. We forgot Rabaud and his Jeremiads in order to concentrate only on the nascent Republic, surrounded by the most monstrous of Coalitions which threatens to stifle it in its cradle; and on the delight which the aristocrats and all Europe would take in conquering us.

THE MARSEILLAIS

You basely abandoned us after exciting our hopes with your short-lived deputations.

THE MAN FROM NIMES

We were acting in good faith – you were the ones who had a fox under your coat; we wanted a Republic and therefore had to accept a Republican Constitution. You were dissatisfied with the Mountain and with what happened on the 31st of May – you ought therefore to have accepted the Constitution in order to dismiss the Mountain by putting an end to its mission.

THE MARSEILLAIS

We also want a Republic, but we want our Constitution to be framed by independent representatives who have a free hand in their work. We want Liberty, but we want it from representatives we can esteem. We do not want our Constitution to protect pillage and anarchy. Our main conditions are : no Club, less emphasis on preparatory assemblies and respect for property.

THE MANUFACTURER FROM MONTPELLIER

It is quite obvious to anyone who is willing to think about it, that one part of Marseilles is counter-revolutionary. They claim that they want the Republic, but that is a veil which has become thinner every day; bit by bit they have been getting you used to the idea of counter-revolution, eventually to lay it bare before you. From the start, the veil which covered it was made of nothing but gauze. Your people were good, but, in time, the whole lot of them would have been perverted were it not for the Guardian Spirit of the Republic which watches over them. Our troops have deserved well of their country in taking up arms against you with so much enthusiasm.

They did not have to imitate the army of 1789, since you are not "the nation". The centre of solidarity is the Convention; that is the true Sovereign, particularly when the people is divided. You have overthrown all the laws, all the conventions. By what right do you break up your Department? Was it Marseilles who established it? By what right has your city's battalion been trampling over the rest of the province? By what right did your national guards presume to move into Avignon? The "district" of this town was in fact the premier lawful body since the Department had been dissolved. What right had you to presume to violate the territory of the Drôme? What makes you think now that this Department does not have the right to call upon public force to defend it? You have thus confounded every conceivable right, you have established anarchy and since you dare to justify your actions by the right of the strongest, you are nothing but brigands and anarchists.

You have set up a popular tribunal; only Marseilles has elected it; it is contrary to every law. It can only be a bloody tribunal since it represents one faction. You have forcibly subjugated the whole of your department to this tribunal. By what right? Aren't you usurping the very authority you take such unjust exception to, where Paris is concerned? Your Section Committee recognises affiliations and connections: so in fact you have a coalition rather like that of the Clubs, against which you are constantly complaining. Your Committee has exercised acts of administration over the communes of Var: this territorial division is new to us . . . In Avignon, you have committed people to prison without authority, without a warrant, without an order from any administrative body. You have abused family privacy, ignored the liberty of the individual; you have cold-bloodedly ordered assassinations in public streets. You have revived those very scenes (whose horror you exaggerate in any case) which afflicted the early days of the Revolution : without inquiries, without trials, without knowing who the victims were, on the word of their enemies alone, you have arrested them, torn them from their children, dragged them through the streets and put them to the sword. You have sacrificed as many as thirty in this way. You have dragged the Statue of Liberty through the mud, you have publicly desecrated her. She has been the object of all manner of insults from lawless youths. You have hacked at the Statue with your swords, you cannot possibly deny it, since it was mid-day and more than two-hundred of your people were seen to be present at this criminal profanation. The procession went along several streets, arrived at the Place de l'Horloge, and continued down the Rue de l'Epicerie, etc., etc.

I had better break off my reflections here, before I lose my temper.

Do you wish your Republic to be like this? You have hindered the progress of our armies by halting the convoys; how can you deny the evidence of so many facts and avoid the title of enemies of our country?

THE SOLDIER

Yes, it has been conclusively proved that the Marseillais have ruined several of our army operations, and wished to suppress liberty, but that is not the point at issue here. The point is to find out what they can hope for and what course is still open to them . . .

THE MARSEILLAIS

I must say we have fewer choices open to us than I thought, but one's strength is greatest when one has resolved to die and we have so resolved rather than bow again under the yoke of those men of blood who govern the state. You know that a drowning man clutches at every straw; so will we, rather than allow ourselves to be butchered . . . yes, we have all taken part in this new revolution, so we would all be sacrificed to vengeance. Two months ago, there was a conspiracy to slaughter four thousand of our worthiest citizens; imagine what excesses would be committed today . . . we will always remember that monster who was nonetheless one of the principal members of the Club : he had a citizen lynched, pillaged his house, and raped his wife after making her drink a cup of her husband's blood.

THE SOLDIER   ·

How disgusting! But is that a fact? I doubt it very much, for you know that no-one believes in rape nowadays . . .

THE MARSEILLAIS

It is true! Rather than submitting to such people, we will fight to the last ditch. We will give ourselves over to the enemy; we will call in the Spaniards. There is no people whose character is less compatible with ours, there are none more detestable to us. Judge the evil of the men we fear by the sacrifice we would make.

THE SOLDIER

Give yourselves over to the Spaniards! We will not leave you the time . . .

THE MARSEILLAIS

We expect them to arrive at our port any day now.

THE MAN FROM NIMES

This threat alone is sufficient for me to see whether it is the "Confederates" or the Mountain that really support the Republic. At one point the Mountain was at its weakest. The disturbance seemed widespread. But did the Mountain ever talk of calling in the enemy? Are you not aware that the fight between the patriots and the Despots of Europe is a fight to the death? If you anticipate their assistance, it is because your leaders have good reasons to expect a welcome from them. But I still have too high an opinion of your people to believe that those of you who wish to carry out such a cowardly scheme form the majority in Marseilles.

THE SOLDIER

Do you really think that you would be doing any great harm to the Republic, and that your threats are at all frightening to us? Let us analyse them.

The Spaniards have no landing forces, their ships cannot even enter your harbour. If you call in the Spaniards, that could help your leaders to make their escape with at least part of their wealth intact. But indignation would be felt throughout the whole Republic, and you would have sixty-thousand troops on your back before the week was out. The Spaniards would carry off all they could and there would still be enough left in Marseilles to enrich the victors.

THE MANUFACTURER FROM MONTPELLIER

If you proved yourselves capable of stooping to such baseness, we should not leave a single stone standing in your superb city. We would make sure that in a month's time, a traveller passing by your ruins would think they were destroyed a hundred years ago.

THE SOLDIER

Believe me, Marseillais, shake off the yoke of the small number of scoundrels who lead you to counter-revolution, re-establish your constituted authorities, accept the Constitution, and give the representatives their liberty, so that they can go to Paris to intercede for you. You have been led astray; it is nothing new for the people to be deceived by a few conspirators and intriguers. In every age, the impetuosity and ignorance of the multitude has been the cause of most civil wars.

THE MARSEILLAIS

Oh! sir, who can get us out of this situation? Will it be the refugees who flock to us from every corner of the Department? They have every reason to act desperately. Will it be those who govern us? Are they not in the same position? Will it be the people? One part does not know where it stands, is blinded and forced to become fanatical. The other part is defenceless, suspicious of everyone, and humiliated; it grieves me to see that there is no remedy for our misfortunes.

THE SOLDIER

At last you are seeing reason. Why should not a similar change of attitude affect a large number of your fellow-citizens who have been misled and who are acting in good faith? Then Albitte, who can only wish to spare French blood, will send you some loyal and well qualified man, we will come to an agreement, and, without a moment's delay, the army will go and make the Spaniard – so proud of his tiny successes – dance the Carmagnole beneath the walls of Perpignan, and Marseilles will still remain the centre of gravity for liberty . . . you will just have to tear a few pages out of your history.

This happy prophecy put us back into a good humour, the Marseillais gladly bought us several bottles of champagne, which completely dissipated all worries and cares. We went to bed at two o'clock in the morning, arranging to meet at breakfast the next day – when the Marseillais had plenty more doubts to express, and I many interesting truths to teach them.

July 29 1793

PART FIVE
Napoleon Writes a Novel

The exact date of Napoleon's most mature attempt at writing fiction is controversial. Clisson and Eugénie *may have been written some time between* New Corsica *and the* Discourse on Happiness *(late 1789 to August 1791). The style bears certain affinities with section two of the* Discourse, *itself a synthesis of everything Napoleon had written before that date. This hypothesis places* Clisson and Eugénie *in roughly the same biographical period as Napoleon's attempt to emulate Rousseau, the super-tramp of Book One of the* Confessions, *during his wanderings around the hill country of Drôme, in February 1791. Alternatively,* Clisson and Eugénie *may have been written between mid-August and mid-September 1795, in Paris. This hypothesis (which is accepted by all the biographers of Napoleon) places the story in the context of Napoleon's affair with Désirée-Eugénie Clary, the daughter of a textile millionaire in Marseilles. Certain cross-references can be made between the content of* Clisson and Eugénie *and the facts of summer 1795. But this assumes that the novel was written at one sitting (which the manuscript evidence contradicts), and that Napoleon was still writing in the style of* Clisson *four years after the* Discourse on Happiness, *which is unlikely.*

This translation has included all the variants, and drafts of *Clisson and Eugénie,* and placed them in the order Napoleon wrote them. They have been translated in full to give some idea of the way in which Napoleon achieved his stylistic effects, and to illustrate how the various drafts lead to the succinct final version. A first draft is denoted by a *, a second draft by a †, and a word or phrase deleted by Napoleon is indicated by brackets and a superior figure.

Introduction

MOST OF the military documents with which the beginning and
the end of *Clisson and Eugénie* were found, were written in the
years 1793-5 : it is usually accepted that Napoleon's romantic
novel dates from the same period – between the siege of Toulon
and his gaining command of the army in Italy. In the biographies which mention *Clisson,* the significance of Napoleon's most
sophisticated attempt at writing fiction is thus seen wholly in
terms of his relationship with Désirée-Eugénie Clary.

After establishing his reputation at the siege of Toulon,
Napoleon was promoted, at the age of twenty-four, to general
of a brigade. But after the events of Thermidor 1794, Napoleon's
Jacobin affiliations became suspect; he had been friendly with
Augustin Robespierre, younger brother of Maximilien and deputy
for Paris in the Convention, and had written *Supper in Beaucaire*
as a pragmatic defence of the Mountain's policies. Napoleon
spent a fortnight under house arrest, during the reaction against
Jacobinism, but characteristically had not committed himself
deeply enough to be detained for long. Subsequently, he was
ordered to proceed to the Vendée, there to take command of
an infantry brigade in the local war against royalist guerrilla
forces : his protests against this "inglorious" task led to a confrontation with the Minister of War, and eventually to the
humiliation of General Bonaparte. He was struck off the army
list for refusing to serve at his post. From May to October 1795,
Napoleon was unemployed, and at one time contemplated throw-
ing himself under a passing carriage. Bourrienne gives a pene-
trating account of Bonaparte's pessimism and sense of frustrated
ambition during this period of inactivity. He spent most of his
time at the Bibliothèque Nationale, and occasionally, when he
could afford it, went to the theatre to see the latest Corneille or
Racine revival. Only the Paris insurrection, and Napoleon's
success in crushing it on the night of XII Vendémiaire of the
year IV (October 4 1795) saved his career. He was restored to

his rank, and the connection he had assiduously maintained with the Director Barras began to pay off. In March 1796, he was finally given command of the Army of Italy. During this unsettled period in Napoleon's life he experienced his first lasting love affair, with Désirée-Eugénie Clary. Joseph Bonaparte had been the first to come into contact with the Clary family in Marseilles : he used his influence to free one of Désirée's relatives who had been imprisoned by the Convention. The Bonapartes soon became acquainted with the Clary family – wealthy royalist textile merchants in Marseilles – and Joseph fell in love with Désirée, the youngest daughter. Her parents had other plans, however, and Joseph was eventually persuaded to marry her elder sister.

After the siege of Toulon, Napoleon arrived in Marseilles with his career apparently assured, and after a few weeks declared *his* love for Désirée. The events of Thermidor made the attentions of the young Jacobin general embarrassing for the Clary family, but after his brief spell of house arrest, Napoleon returned to become engaged to Désirée. He had set his heart on a peaceful domestic existence, as far removed from the vicissitudes of politics as possible. Napoleon returned to Paris in order to cancel his posting to the Vendée, and found himself in disgrace once again. Désirée's mother forced her to write and break off the engagement.

Clisson and Eugénie was supposedly written between mid-August and mid-September 1795, when the interplay of events between Napoleon's public and private life had recently borne a striking resemblance to the plot of his novel. The success of Toulon was followed by a period of unemployment when Napoleon/Clisson could re-assess his attitudes and try to settle into bourgeois family life. The love affair with Désirée-Eugénie was conceived in Rousseauistic terms, and it was only a direct confrontation between personal and professional responsibilities which caused the destruction of the idyll. But there are dangers in this method of dating *Clisson and Eugénie*. If comparisons between plot details and the chronology of Napoleon's life provide the basic evidence, then *Clisson* could have been written at a still later date, when Napoleon had discovered Josephine's infidelities during the Italian Campaign – an unlikely hypothesis.

It is also hazardous to date *Clisson* with reference to Napoleon's philosophical development: in the *Dialogue on Love* (1791) he suggests that Des Mazis repress his extreme and immature emotions in favour of fulfilling his social and political obligations. Clisson's dilemma is more personal, and seems to suggest Napoleon's own first experiences of love. But as we have seen, the *Dialogue on Love* makes more sense as an intellectual game, at odds with Napoleon's intimate feelings contained in the *Journal*.

The pitfalls of trying to date a work of literature with reference to the biography of the author are even more apparent in Rousseau's *La Nouvelle Héloïse* on which *Clisson* is to a large extent based. For many years literary critics tried to date the central sections of *La Nouvelle Héloïse* in terms of Rousseau's description (in the *Confessions*) of his "affair" with Sophie d'Houdetot. There are cross-references between Rousseau's letters of 1757-8 and the style of "St. Preux"; the chronology of writing suggested by the author himself seems to fit this pattern. But Rousseau makes errors of detail in the *Confessions*, and his reminiscences about the relationship are sometimes inaccurate. It is more likely that Rousseau had written a substantial part of the early sections of the novel, and prepared some plan of the middle sections when he became acquainted with Sophie: thereafter, his life and the "rêverie" became inextricably mixed. The whole process is considerably more complex than would at first appear. In Napoleon's case this method is also misleading: on June 19 1799, Napoleon told the Directory of his struggle against a false prophet in Egypt, who called himself "the angel El Mahdy". The story bears notable resemblances to the plot of *The Mask of the Prophet*, which we know was written ten years before!

Frédéric Masson, in the Introduction to his *Napoléon dans sa jeunesse* places *Clisson* in the same creative period as *New Corsica* (1788-9) because·of similarities in style and handwriting. Nada Tomiche, in her *Napoléon Ecrivain*, accepts the date 1795 without question, and F. G. Healey, in his *Rousseau et Napoléon*, comes to the same conclusion after a detailed summary of the evidence. The most recent biography of Napoleon, by Vincent Cronin, not only dates *Clisson* with reference to Napoleon's affair with Désirée, but quotes a passage from the story as evidence of Napoleon's attitude to the two Clary sisters. The style of *Clisson* – an amalgam of Rousseau's inflated imagery and an army bulletin – seems to place the work before 1795. Given Napoleon's tendency to be influenced by writers he considered as important at any one time, and his use of recurring images in those works he attempted to write (often concurrently) in periods of sustained creative activity, internal evidence suggests that *Clisson* was written between *New Corsica* and the preparations for the *Discourse to the Academy of Lyon* (roughly between June 1789 and August 1791).

In the second part of this *Discourse*, Napoleon tries to vary his style as much as possible, while sustaining a façade of elegance. He does this, as we have seen, by drawing on his own experiences (homesickness, wounded amour-propre) and by using most of the works written before the *Discourse* (*New Corsica, Parallel between Love of Glory and Love of Country* etc.) as the basis for a series of "tableaux" which illustrate aspects of the definition of sentiment. This creates an impression of stylistic variety, which Napoleon can subsequently shrug aside with apparent modesty : "There is no reader who cannot supply his own (examples)". In this context, the thematic and stylistic cross-references with *Clisson* are crucial for dating purposes. Napoleon's descriptions of the "melancholy of nature" in the sea-shore tableau, and of the sensation of "withdrawing into oneself to meditate on the origin of nature while savouring its most exquisite delights" in the shepherd's hut tableau, are similar to the first draft of *Clisson*, in particular the passage where the hero is described in his wanderings around the Champvert countryside.

A whole series of "tableaux" in the *Discourse to the Academy of Lyon* directly cross-refer with the equivalent sections in *Clisson*. The following is a selection taken from the *Discourse* :

"Returning from a long walk, have you ever been surprised by nightfall? Have you, by the light of silver rays reached the perfect silence of the Universe? . . . You savour the delights of coolness and the salutary balm of rêverie."

"Have you ever been out in your flowering thickets or in a vast forest at seven in the morning? . . . you will be able to pass whole hours alone without being able to tear yourself away, or having to put up with the chatter of irritating people who come to importune you."

"Man may well surround himself with all the trappings of fortune, but as soon as his sentiment takes flight from his heart, boredom possesses it, sadness, black melancholy and despair succeed each other, and if this state continues he kills himself."

Later in the *Discourse*, Napoleon describes a "young beauty who has just entered her sixteenth year" (the same age as Eugénie when Clisson first meets her, and, by coincidence, as Désirée when Napoleon was first introduced), a "young girl" whose lover has died, and an "adolescent" whose fortunes are followed in the various stages of his life. First comes the "dawn of passion" (described at the beginning of the *Discourse* as part of the cycle of man's development), then a period during which the young man is a victim of the "prejudice of passion" and consequently neglects his social and political duties, and finally the "virile age" where "ambition has mastered him" and although he may reach the "helm of affairs", he will probably not feel satisfied with his lot.

Napoleon synthesises all he has written in Part II of the *Discourse* in an extended comparison between simple melodic music (such as the *Devin du Village*) which can remind one of the "happiness of country life and the innocence of the Golden Age", and those pieces which "should be proscribed", which are "captivating for a moment only to deal the death-blow to virtue and happiness straightaway". This comparison is an obvious reminder of the colourful musical image which is used to differentiate Amélie and Eugénie.

The *Discourse* contains echoes of Berville's "dawn of passion", of Clisson's experiences in the countryside far away from the "petty formalities" and the "empty logic of the gossips", and of the description in *Clisson* of an adolescent who is "born for happiness" but who has "as yet found only glory". The following passage from *Clisson* gives some idea of the many points of contact between the two works.

He knew no more agreeable pastime than to wander in the woods. There he found contentment, he could defy small-mindedness and rise above folly and the baseness of humanity. Sometimes, on silver starlit banks he surrendered to the desires of his trembling heart. He could no longer tear himself from the sweet, but melancholy spectacle of a moonlit night. He would often remain there until the moon had vanished from sight and darkness had effaced his rêverie.

Clisson's awakening to the beauties of the Lyon countryside, where Napoleon himself wrote in August 1786 that "I would have liked to spend my life there", and where the Academy was situated for which he was writing his ambitious *Discourse on Sentiment,* could be transposed unaltered into the scheme of "tableaux" in Part II of the *Discourse.* Such evidence is not, of course, conclusive, but at least provides the basis for a working hypothesis that *Clisson and Eugénie* was written between 1789 and 1791.

Some time may have elapsed between the first and final drafts of the work. We know that Napoleon had access to the manuscript during most of his early life and the original draft contains corrections which suggest that it was written on at least two separate occasions. In the title, the word Eugénie is written clearly, then crossed out at a later date (conceivably when the affair with Désirée-Eugénie was finished), and in the description of Clisson's entry into Champvert society, Napoleon at first gave his hero's acquaintance a proper name, then changed his mind (possibly because this gave the incident too much specificity) and substituted the phrase "a friend of his". We have seen the dangers of dating the story with reference to the name "Eugénie". In fact, Napoleon's descriptions of the two young girls in *Clisson* may not have been taken from life at all. There seem to be certain points of contact between the characters of "Amélie", "Eugénie" and the Clary sisters, but the heroine of the story bears little resemblance to Désirée. "Eugénie", in Napoleon's story, has the character and physical appearance of Désirée's sister, Julie (Joseph's wife). She was apparently timid, brittle, and without the beauty of her younger sister. Désirée, on the other hand, had a great deal in common with "Amélie". She was attractive, vivacious, irresponsible and domineering. She willingly transferred her affections from Joseph to Napoleon, and accepter her parents' advice – apparently without question – to break off her subsequent engagement to the penniless Corsican. While Napoleon refused to call her Désirée because the name suggested to him the desires of the flesh, she chided him because his letters were too cold and brusque. The name "Clisson" may have been inspired by that of a commander of the French army under Charles VII : the character in Napoleon's story is representative of the conflict between military and domestic values, and in this capacity is more of a paradigmatic soldier-figure than a specific person.

The quality of the handwriting varies – the paragraph which deals with the impact of married life on Eugénie's character is written in bold characters, and is fairly easy to decipher, while the section which leads up to the engagement of Clisson and Eugénie is full of crossings out, abbreviations, and mis-spelt words. This section was obviously written at great speed, and in the original manuscript runs roughly like this : "et ils s'aperci dans peu de jours que le ames etoit fait pour s'aimer. voire sourire Eugenie, apprecier ses qualités, admirer les chs de sa pers et de soncharactère en fait beauté de la veh de consentir de lui dire sa parole".

Another passage, which appears a few lines after this descrip tion, shows the difficulties Napoleon experienced in choosing the correct word. He has several attempts at creating a balanced, rhythmic sentence, but is indecisive about the most effective order in which his short phrases should appear. In the following extract, the brackets indicate crossings out.

(Clisson et Eugénie furent unis. L'amour, la volupté, le sent, la confusion des ames – tout court a la bonheur)
Tout ce que l'amour a de plus louable, le sentiment le plus doux, la volupte le plus esquis inonda le coe de ces trop he amans. (jours perdu aux) epanchement tendre, union des coes, confusion des pensées, (des ames. Confusion) protestations sincerement et vraiment (bien) sentis, desires sures, lien des am, . . . les jours de leur bonheur.

There is a large ink smudge across the last few words of this passage, so the problems of transcription are acute.

Despite the variable style, derivative imagery and clumsy

construction, *Clisson and Eugénie* is Napoleon's most mature attempt at story-telling. Narrative and descriptive passages are balanced, and the episodic nature of the work may be due to a conscious attempt to keep the story moving at a consistently fast pace : Napoleon later criticised Rousseau for allowing himself to digress, and divide the reader's attention in *La Nouvelle Héloïse*. The central section of *Clisson,* which corresponds to the "domestic economy" section in *La Nouvelle Héloïse* is brief and to the point. Instead of a long discussion on the running of a rural estate, Napoleon writes three short descriptive phrases, and even manages to include a Voltairean aside in his version of the agricultural economy of Clarens :

"By day they never left each other's side; raising their children, cultivating their garden, organising their household . . ."

Clisson and Eugénie

FROM BIRTH, Clisson was destined for war. While still a child he was well versed in the lives of the great generals. He studied the principles of military science at a time when others of his age were still at school, and in pursuit of prostitutes. From the time he was old enough to bear arms, he rendered each step remarkable by some dazzling achievement. Though still an adolescent, he reached the highest rank in the army. Constant good fortune re-inforced his genius. One victory followed another, and his name became known to the people, as that of one of their most beloved champions.*†

* From his birth, Clisson had a pronounced taste for war. As a child, the sight of a helmet, sword or drum would reveal in him that dedication of his nature which had destined him to attain the highest ranks of the army while still an adolescent. He absorbed the principles of the art of war at an age when one is commonly occupied only with story-books. Fascinated by glory, he long disdained all other passions : love he despised, he scorned the idea of chance. In spite of this, his silent heart, so long possessed by the fires of war, came to know other needs.

† From his birth, Clisson had a pronounced taste for war. He read the lives of great men at the age when one reads story-books. He studied the principles of military science at a time when others of his age were still at school. He rose swiftly through the ranks, each step remarkable for some dazzling achievement. He attained the highest ranks of the army while still an adolescent.

Envy and calumny are base instincts which assail growing reputations, cause so many useful men to succumb, and smother so much genius. Ability, composure, courage and resolution do nothing but increase the number of Clisson's enemies, and give offence to men, who, because of their position, ought to sway opinion on his account. His greatness of soul was called pride;

147

he was reproached for his resolution. Disgusted with his triumphs which increased the number of his enemies without gaining him friends, Clisson felt the need to withdraw into himself. For the first time in his life, he began to look at his career, his tastes and his condition. He spent a month in the country, near Lyon, with an acquaintance. Devoted since childhood to war, he had been carried away by the whirlwind of events, and ever dominated by the power of his inclinations. His soul, possessed and absorbed by these constant occupations, bore as yet no impression of other interests and values.*†

* In spite of this, his soul was not satisfied.
The pain that malicious envy can inflict, grieved him bitterly. Like all men, Clisson had been born for happiness; he had as yet found only glory. He had despised love. But he met Eugénie. One day the war ended, and he met Eugénie.
Eugénie was sixteen years old. She was gentle, good and spirited. She had fine eyes and an undistinguished figure. Without being plain, she was not a beauty. Goodness, tenderness and a sweet temper were all an essential part of her. Clisson had despised women and love; but now he chose to investigate this new reaction within himself – gentleness can make no resistance.
Clisson frightens Eugénie. Stern Clisson is in love.
Clisson's heart, accustomed to victories and great enterprises, soon gave his passion the stamp of his distinctive vigour and inflexibility. Eugénie realised that it was her fate to become part of this great man's destiny, and promised him eternal love. Clisson promised likewise.

† Clisson's heart yearned for happiness, but so far had only cast off the illusions of glory.
He seldom remained indoors.
His friend was a well established figure in local circles, and was always receiving guests : Clisson could not accustom himself to the petty formalities. His vivid imagination, his fervent heart, his rigorous intellect and his unbending disposition inevitably wearied of the charms of coquetry, the shallowness of courtesy, the empty logic of the gossips and the conventions of satire. He knew nothing about intrigue. He understood nothing of word-play. He was used to a cruder way of life, and his faculties were absorbed by a single thought, which he could neither define nor comprehend as yet,

but which completely mastered his being. Accustomed to hardship, he felt the need for action and a great deal of exercise.

He knew no more agreeable pastime than to wander in the woods. There he found contentment, he could defy small-mindedness and rise above folly and the baseness of humanity.

Sometimes, on silver starlit banks, he surrendered to the desires of his trembling heart. He could no longer tear himself from the sweet, but melancholy spectacle of a moonlit night. He would often remain there until the moon had vanished from sight, and darkness had effaced his rêverie; sad and uneasy, he would then depart in search of a much needed repose.

Reflection yielded to rêverie. He perceived, with a hitherto unimagined pleasure, the varied spectacle of nature : the birth and death of each new day, birds singing, the murmuring of water and the patchwork of meadows.

He spent whole hours meditating deep in the woods, and in the evening he would stay there until midnight, lost in rêveries, by the light of the silver evening star. He often went to the spring at Alles, an hour's journey from Champvert, where the waters are extremely cool at a certain time of year, between four and six in the morning.

This withdrawal into himself caused him to realise that war was not the only purpose in life, that there were other inclinations than those which lead to destruction.

The art of caring for mankind, bettering their lot, and making them happy is fully equal to that of destroying them.

He wanted to collect his thoughts for a moment, to create some order out of this tangle of ideas which for several days had been tormenting his spirit. He withdrew from the army and hastened to Champvert, near Lyon, where he sought hospitality of a country gentleman, a friend of his.

This part of the countryside, one of the finest surrounding the city, combined all that human ingenuity and the beauty of nature could offer.

Clisson marvelled at the absorbing spectacle of the birth and death of each new day, at the course of the night-star, scattering silver light over thicket and field.

Everything made a fresh and hitherto unimagined impression

on his heart: the varieties of season, of landscape, the song of the birds, the murmuring of water . . .

However, he was only seeing what he had seen a thousand times before, without feeling anything, without being impressed.

Poor Clisson . . . Your soul, so beset by illusion, by impulse, by anxiety is dulled to the beauty and insensible to the pleasure of nature.

By nature a sceptic, Clisson became melancholy: reflection had given way to rêverie. He had nothing to look forward to, nothing to hope or to fear. This state of passivity, so new to a man of his genius, could easily have led to a state of stupor, without his knowing it. From the break of day, he wandered around the countryside, constantly brooding over his new experiences.

He often went to the Spa at Alles, a league away from where he was staying.

He would spend entire mornings there, observing mankind, wandering through the forest or reading some worthwhile book.

One day, there happened to be a few people nearby and Clisson caught sight of two pretty girls, who seemed to be taking great pleasure in their walk. They had just made their way there unaccompanied, with all the gaiety and vivacity of sixteen-year-olds.

Amélie had a beautiful figure, beautiful eyes, a beautiful complexion, beautiful hair and she was seventeen. Eugénie, the younger by a year, was less beautiful.

When she looked at you, Amélie seemed to be saying: "You are in love with me, but you are not the only one; I have plenty of other men. You must understand that the only way to please me is to flatter me. I enjoy compliments and I love affected speeches!"

Eugénie never looked hard at men. When she smiled sweetly, she revealed the most beautiful teeth imaginable. If a hand was held out to her, she gave hers timidly and withdrew it swiftly. One might think it provocative to display so fleetingly the prettiest of hands where the whiteness of the skin contrasted with the blue of the veins.

Amélie was like a piece of French music, that can be enjoyed because the chord sequences are readily understood and pleasing to everyone; most people can appreciate harmony.

Eugénie was like the song of the nightingale, or like a piece by Paësiello which pleases only sensitive souls, whose melody enraptures and impassions those souls made to feel it deeply, while appearing commonplace to many people.

Amélie conquered most young men : she commanded love.

Eugénie could please only the passionate man, who does not love for form's sake, as a gallant, but who loves with all the ardour of heartfelt emotion.

Amélie inspired love by her beauty.

Eugénie was destined to kindle a powerful passion in one single heart, a passion worthy . . . of heroes.

Amélie's fine complexion and eyes were worthy of Clisson's attentions. He contrived to make an opportunity to speak with her, and escorted them both back to their house in the country, where he requested permission to come and visit them alone sometimes.

He was completely captivated by the pretty girls he had just encountered.[1] He could not weary of recalling Amélie's likeness to mind, of remembering her words. He let himself linger over that seductive image, but the vivid memory of silent, modest Eugénie pursued him; it exercised some strange sway over his heart which dulled the pleasure of lovely Amélie's smiles.

The two girls, for their part, had reacted in very different ways. Amélie reproached Eugénie for her failure to dissimulate the little pleasure that the [2]stranger's conversation had given her. She thought him sombre, but distinguished in person, and sincere. Eugénie thought that Amélie had been too forward. Her heart was ill at ease, and she found herself in this disquieting position : she could not doubt that she had conceived a great

[1] (On the way back)
[2] (the sight of this man)

aversion for the stranger, an aversion which she could neither explain nor justify.

The next day Amélie failed – despite her stubborn insistence – to persuade Eugénie to accompany her to Alles. Eugénie could not think clearly. The moment Amélie had left, she got up, wrote to her sister, and began to think about the stranger.

Clisson arrived before Amélie. They opened their hearts to each other like old acquaintances. The free atmosphere of the Spa and the gaiety of the place banished all formality, and all etiquette. They walked home together happier than ever. They discussed everything, criticised the country lovers they saw, and the amiable and beautiful and gay Amélie went home with a very high opinion of [3]Clisson, whom she found ungallant but very pleasant.

She talked of nothing but Clisson all day, and made Eugénie agree to go to the Spa the next day. Eugénie, for her part, had given much thought to something the stranger had said. She did not know whether to hate him or esteem him.[4]

They had all made a tacit rendezvous – Clisson did not disappoint them. As soon as he caught sight of Amélie, he was annoyed to see that her friend was with her. Eugénie, for her part, listened without speaking, or else replied without thinking what she was saying. She gazed fixedly at the stranger; she could never tire of watching him.

What sort of man is he?

Why does he look so sombre and pensive?

Can one not see in his eyes the maturity of age, and in his physiognomy the languor of adolescence?

And then she was annoyed to see him so engrossed in Amélie.

She pretended to be tired,[5] and persuaded the rest of the party to start walking homewards. On the way, they encountered a gentleman who had occasionally met the girls before[6].

[3] (of herself.)

[4] (She wanted him more . . . to dream . . . the basis on which she should pursue him . . .)

[5] ("I am tired")

[6] (A great friend of the household)

This gentleman was astonished to see Clisson with Amélie, and saw no reason to compliment him on it.

"Monsieur Clisson", said Amélie.

"Excuse me", said Eugénie, interrupting, "we have heard a great deal about you, I would like so very much to know you better."

The expression of her voice and physiognomy went straight to Clisson's heart. He looked at her more closely[7] . . . and in a few days they realised that they were made to love each other. The sight of Eugénie smiling, appreciating his qualities, admiring the charms of his appearance and his character – all this gave beauty to the vehemence with which she consented to pledge him her troth.

This was the work of the most ardent and impetuous love that has ever moved a man's heart. Eugénie, who had dedicated her heart to friendship, who had thought herself insensible to love, now felt all its fire. Clisson had no complaints; he no longer troubled himself with men, wickedness or war. Henceforth, he lived only for Eugénie. They met frequently. Their souls joined sincerely together. They surmounted every obstacle and were united forever.

[8]Everything most laudable in love, most sweet in sentiment, most exquisite in voluptuousness welled up in the hearts of these too happy lovers[9]. Tender effusions, union of hearts, confusion of thoughts, [10]sincere and truly felt protestations, lasting desires, the bonds of love – all these combined to make up the days of their happiness.

Clisson banished war from his mind, scorned the time when he had lived without Eugénie, without drawing breath for her alone. For the sake of love, he renounced all thought of glory.

---

[7] (Clisson suddenly opened his eyes wide, and fell silent . . . gallant Clisson! For his part, he could only stare more fixedly at Eugénie. Their eyes met . . . their hearts united.)

[8] (Clisson and Eugénie were united. Everything paved the way for their happiness – love, voluptuousness, sentiment, confusion of hearts.)

[9] (Days lost to)

[10] (Souls, confusion)

The months, the years slipped by[11] as quickly as the hours. They had children and remained lovers. Eugénie loved as steadfastly as she was loved. There was no pleasure, no grief, no solicitude they did not share. It was as if nature had given them the same heart, same soul, same sentiments. At night, Eugénie always slept with her head on her lover's shoulder, or in his arms. By day they never left each other's side; raising their children, cultivating their garden, organising their household. Eugénie had avenged Clisson for the injustice of man, which he remembered only as in a dream.

The fashionable world, and even the people who lived nearby had forgotten, completely forgotten what Clisson had once been. Living as they did in such rustic seclusion, near to the sea and to nature, both Clisson and Eugénie were considered to be as mad as they were misanthropic.[12] Only the poor appreciated and blessed them. That consoled them for the vexations of fools.

Although Eugénie was twenty-two years old by now, she felt as if she was still in the first year of her marriage. Never perhaps had two separate souls more closely united two hearts. Never had capricious love linked two such differing characters. The companionship of such a worthy man as Clisson had made Eugénie more accomplished. Her talents had blossomed, and her tender, vulnerable sentiments had taken on that character of strength and energy so essential for the mother of Clisson's children. Clisson was no longer sombre, no longer sad; his character had contracted the gentleness and sweetness of that of his beloved. Military honours, which had accustomed him to command, had made him proud and sometimes hard. Eugénie's love made him more considerate and flexible.

[11] (slipped by like)
[12] (uncivilised)

They rarely mixed in society; they were little known, even to their neighbours. The only time they came into contact with the outside world was when they were protecting the poor.*

* (One night. For some time.) Eugénie was 22. The companionship of so worthy a man, the virtue and unbroken serenity of her life had bestowed even more grace upon her physiognomy; hence her charms had been enhanced. Faithful lover, tender mother, protectress of the poor, your life made up of so many tranquil things should always remain serene . . . For some time, a kind of foreboding had been troubling her. Her eyes became moist with tears, her heart was heavy. She seized and embraced Clisson, clasped him in her arms; she could no longer tear herself away from him. Melancholy by day, uneasy and over-affectionate by night, poor Eugénie dreaded an uncertain future which could only disturb her mind.

It was in the month of June. The suffocating heat of the day enhanced the dazzling beauty of the nights. The heat was excessive. Terrible storm-clouds hung menacingly over the horizon. Rain, thunder and lightning blackened and illuminated the sky.

Eugénie dissolved into tears . . .

She clasped her husband tightly to her breast. Sophie began to weep at her mother's grief and hid in her skirts, embracing her mother's knees with her little hands.*

* Eugénie could never look at her children without being moved to tears of tenderness.

"Oh Clisson," she said one day, holding Sophie in her arms, "what dismal future awaits us! If your heart ever ceases to be faithful to me, pluck this life from my breast."

Clisson, who was bound irrevocably to Eugénie by love, disposition and esteem, was grieved at her distress, and soothed her fears.

"Eugénie," he would often reply, "the day that I first linked your destiny to mine, I swore to defend your life and support your weakness. Your husband will never cease to be your lover. Yes, he will not change . . . he will always live for you, he will never survive your loss."

"Clisson, your future is uncertain, and my soul is beset by fears of impending doom. If you must cease to love me, take the life of your Eugénie with that same hand that once so lovingly caressed me."

Clisson, whom esteem, love and disposition bound irrevocably to Eugénie, grieved at the distress of his beloved. He neglected nothing to restore her to reason and happiness. He took Sophie in his arms.

"My Eugénie, I hereby swear eternal love, on the life of our Sophie. But cease to afflict me. Must you alarm yourself while my heart is so at ease?"

They continued their conversation long into the darkness of the night. They went to bed very late. They had just gone to sleep when Clisson was awakened by the sound of approaching horses.

He got up and saw one of his old couriers, who brought him a letter from the government. It was an order to leave for Paris within twenty-four hours, where he was to be charged with an important mission that the government wished to entrust to his abilities.

Wretched Eugénie, you are lost in sleep as your beloved is torn from you!

"So, the terrible mystery is explained!" she cried. "My fears have been realised!

"Oh Clisson, you are abandoning me. Once more you will encounter the caprice, the folly of men, events and fortune. Farewell, my happiness. Farewell those blissful days, so brittle and so infinitely short : they are worthless now."

She was pale, exhausted and lifeless.

Clisson was equally upset.

However, he had to leave.

Soon he was at the head of an army. He could take no step without remembering Eugénie and re-living the story of his love in his memory.

His name was a sure sign of victory. His talents and good fortune made him great.

Ever successful, he surpassed even the hopes of the people and of the army who owed him their success.

Still so young, so useful to his family and country; must the story of Clisson end here?

He had been separated from his beloved for several years. Not a day passed when he did not receive tender letters which sustained his courage and nourished his love.

In an action where he was forced to risk himself, he was dangerously wounded. Public rumour exaggerated his misfortune. He despatched Berville, one of his officers, to break the news to his wife, and keep her company until his wounds were completely healed.

Berville had reached the dawn of passion. He had never been in love. He was like a tired and lost traveller who casts his eyes round at the end of a long journey to find somewhere he can rest for the night. He was in search of somewhere to settle his heart.

He went to see Eugénie, mingled his tears with hers, and shared her worries. All day long they talked of Clisson and his misfortunes.

His youthful heart, untutored in the ways of passion, believed itself to be motivated by tender friendship : but a passion all the more violent because it was strange and completely hidden had already taken possession of him.

He worshipped Eugénie. She was in no way suspicious of her husband's friend.

Already she wrote less frequently, and at less length.

Clisson began to be tormented by doubts.

He had recovered from his glorious wounds. But a restlessness that he could not conceal betrayed the ferment of his mind. Eugénie no longer wrote to him. Eugénie no longer loved him. Berville's letters to him were forced and unenthusiastic. Day and night he brooded on his cruel misfortune.

His first impulse was to ride to Champvert and rescue Eugénie from misery and disgrace. But the army, his orders . . . and his country had placed him where he was.

"It is two o'clock in the morning. Everything is prepared for death. Orders have been given. They are making ready for battle. Tomorrow, how much blood will flow over this ground! But Eugénie, what will you say, what will you do, what will become of you?

Rejoice in my death, curse my memory, and prosper . . ."

At daybreak the drums began to roll. Fires around bivouac tents died out. The columns began to move forward. The flanks were attacked by cavalry charges. Death walked in the ranks.

"How many ill-fated men regret their life and still desire to preserve it? I alone wish to put an end to my life. It was Eugénie who gave it to me."

They came to inform him that the right flank had been routed. The centre was being repulsed . . . and was fighting at close quarters. Shortly after, came the news that the centre was victorious, but that on the left flank . . . fresh troops had appeared on the battlefield.

"Farewell the chosen arbiter of my life. Farewell, companion of my happiest days! In your arms I tasted supreme happiness. I have exhausted life and all its blessings. What had I to hope for in times to come but satiety and sorrow? At twenty-six years of age I have exhausted the ephemeral pleasures of fame, but in your love, I have delighted in the sweetest sentiments of a man's life.

"The memory of this rends my heart. May you live happily, forgetting wretched Clisson!

"Embrace my sons; may they not have the fervent spirit of their father to become, like him, victims of mankind, of glory and of love!"

He folded his letter, ordered an aide-de-camp to carry it to Eugénie without delay, and straightaway placed himself at the head of a squadron . . . rushed headlong into the mêlée . . . and expired pierced by a thousand blows.

Epilogue

Las Cases, in his *Mémorial de Sainte-Hélène*, writes of his discussions with the exiled Emperor about literature:

> IN READING Vertot's *Roman Revolutions,* of which in other respects the Emperor thinks highly, he found the declamations much too diffuse. This was his constant complaint against every work he took up; he had in his youth, he said, been much to blame in this respect himself. He may justly be said to have thoroughly reformed afterwards. He amused himself with striking out the superfluous phrases in Vertot, and the result was that after these erasures, the work appeared much more energetic and animated. "It would certainly be a most valuable and successful labour" said he, "if any man of taste and discernment would devote his time to reducing the principal works in our language in this manner. I know nobody but Montesquieu who would escape these curtailments". He often looked into Rollin, whom he thought diffuse and too credulous . . . He complained of our classical works, and of the time which our young people are compelled to lose in reading such bad books. They were composed by rhetoricians, and mere professors, he said, whereas such immortal subjects, the basis of all our knowledge throughout life, ought to have been written and edited by statesmen and men of the world. The Emperor had excellent ideas on this subject: the want of time alone prevented him from carrying them into execution.
>
> The Emperor was still more dissatisfied with our French historians; he could not bear to read any of them . . . "Our history", said the Emperor, "should either be in four or five volumes, or in a hundred."

Napoleon seems to have passed many of his long leisure hours on St. Helena, by cutting or summarising a selection of the novels he had read for the first time in his youth: he tried to make the author's point (narrative or didactic) more apparent. According to Grand Marshal Bertrand's *Cahiers de Sainte-Hélène,* on February 8, 1821 the Emperor read two hundred pages of Bernardin de St-Pierre's *Paul et Virginie* and then proceeded to calculate the heroine's household budget in terms of the number of domestic servants she employed, her capital outlay, and the maximum profit from her land. He based his calculations on the fact that Dominique, the negro slave, belonged to Madame de la Tour : in fact, he was employed by Marguerite, her neighbour.

He re-read Rousseau's *La Nouvelle Héloïse* several times during his exile, and his attitude to this romantic novel, which he had devoured in his youth, changed considerably. Las Cases recounts a conversation he had with the Emperor on December 7, 1815. "He began to read *La Nouvelle Héloïse,* frequently remarking on the ingenuity and force of the arguments, the elegance of the style and expression : he read for upwards of two hours . . . the enchantment seemed to seize him. At length, he laid down the book, and went out into the garden. 'Really' said he, as we walked along, 'this work is not without fire; it moves, it rouses the feelings'." (See Healey, op. cit., and the same author's *Rousseau et Napoléon.*)

Baron Gourgaud was present when Napoleon discussed *La Nouvelle Héloïse* again, on May 12 1817. By this time, the Emperor had become critical of certain themes in Rousseau's novel. He complained that the plot suspended disbelief too much – he could not accept that Julie's husband, Baron Wolmar, would behave in such a detached and unemotional manner in allowing his wife's ex-lover to stay at Clarens : Rousseau's famous ménage à trois situation seemed unconvincing. The "tests" which Wolmar makes Saint-Preux undergo, to exorcise the young tutor's love for Julie – which involve time-games, de-sacralisation of geographical locations which have romantic associations, and a complete stage-management of Saint-Preux's existence along the lines of Rousseau's projected *Morale Sensitive ou le Matérialisme du Sage* – seemed to Napoleon "utter nonsense". One of the most famous Swiss locations for the story – the rocks of Meillerie on the banks of Lake Geneva – had certainly lost its romantic association for Napoleon. In 1816, the Emperor told Las Cases that he had destroyed these rocks to prepare a route to the Simplon Pass.

In Geneva, there is a copy of *La Nouvelle Héloïse* believed to have been one of the volumes in Napoleon's travelling campaign library; this copy was also taken to St. Helena. Part of the camp library provided Napoleon's staple diet of reading during his exile, while the rest of the books remained at the Tuileries. The edition contains the stamp "du Cabinet de l'Empereur", and is annotated in his handwriting. Since the Emperor's changing attitudes towards Rousseau's novel in many ways reflect his wider views on both the writing and reading of fiction, they are worth describing in detail. (See O. Reverdin's article in *Annales . . . Jean-Jacques Rousseau* 1943-5.)

The first twenty-eight pages of the third volume, and page thirteen of the fourth were corrected, in pencil, by Napoleon on St. Helena; these alterations mainly consist of deletions and marginal notes. For example, from Part Four, Letter One of *La Nouvelle Héloïse,* which is written from Julie de Wolmar to Claire d'Orbe, the Emperor deletes twenty lines of text, and substitutes five short linking words of his own to retain the sense. In most cases, he deletes single adjectives, subordinate clauses, parentheses or repetitive emotional outbursts. He cuts an entire section of the second paragraph of the letter – which begins with the words "as one grows older all one's sensations begin to concentrate" – and writes in the margin "this is unsound". At the beginning of Part Four, Letter Two, which is the reply to the previous letter, Napoleon crosses out seven lines of the third paragraph – which concern the friendship of the widow Claire for Julie – and simply adds the word "que" to link the two ends of the section. Finally, Napoleon turned to the second letter of the fifth part (from Saint-Preux to Milord Edward Bomston) and crossed out four lines from the fourth paragraph. This deletion was probably not made for stylistic reasons; it seems that Napoleon disagreed with Rousseau's direct comparison between the idyllic domestic economy of Clarens, and the refined manners of fashionable French Society. Although Napoleon was deeply influenced in his preparation for the *Discours de Lyon,* by Rousseau's ideas on the re-definition of accepted all-purpose terms ("fortune", "honour" etc) and by the Genevan's comparative method of describing *direct* and *indirect* political relationships, he apparently considered the play on the word "vivre" out of place here. Rousseau gives the various stages of the plot of *La Nouvelle Héloïse* a social resonance by cunningly placing descriptions of other societies/ communities – the Valais, Paris, the colonies, Geneva – into the main body of the narrative. This comparative method, together with Rousseau's attempt to re-define "à la mode" words, is most apparent in the description of Clarens. After Napoleon has made his corrections (here indicated by brackets), the relevant paragraph reads as follows:

> If I had to say precisely what they do in this household to be happy, I would think I had given a good reply if I said "they know how to *live* there", (not in the sense that the word is used in France – where it means having a certain way with other people, laid down by fashion) but to live the life of man (for which he is born), the life of which you have spoken to me . . . which one does not consider lost at the day of death.

Apart from this example, Napoleon's corrections are made to keep the action moving, to cut down the amount of space devoted to "rêverie", or to remove a "digression" which seemed to distract from the major theme of the individual letter. Interestingly enough, the most recent English translation of *La Nouvelle Héloïse* (1968), which has been "abridged for the modern reader", contains several of the same deletions. The edition states that "abridgement is eminently justified, for the author continually interrupted the flow of the plot with repetitious digressions". Napoleon could hardly have put it better himself.

The Emperor's change of attitude to this romantic novel is revealing: when in his most subdued and depressed moods, Napoleon seems to have enjoyed reading such works; he could appreciate the sentimental "rêveries". Madame de Montholon thought that "in our position here, reading such stories stirs one's mind too much", and on these occasions, Napoleon's literary imagination would be awakened. On July 12 1816, he spoke about *The Man in the Iron Mask* to Gourgaud. "The Governor of Pignerol – the prison where the Man in the Iron

Mask was confined, was called Bompars. This man married his daughter to a mysterious prisoner, supposed to be the brother of Louis XIV, and then sent the couple to Corsica, under the name 'Buonaparte'. The children of this marriage were his ancestors . . . 'I had but to say the word for people to believe this story' says the Emperor". In more rational moments, Napoleon tried to detach himself from the issues, and adopt some critical stance to the novels he was reading.

Whether or not Napoleon really read *La Nouvelle Héloïse* at the age of nine – something of an achievement for a Corsican! – the novel was one of the select few which Napoleon took on his campaigns. It was the only work of Rousseau he constantly travelled with, and the rest of that section of the library included Goethe's *Young Werther,* ten volumes of the Abbé Prévost's works, a varied selection of English novels (including those of Richardson), four volumes of Voltaire's stories, and Bernardin de St. Pierre's *Paul et Virginie.*

It is difficult to assess whether Napoleon saw how *La Nouvelle Héloïse* cross-referred with Rousseau's other, more political writings. At the time of his extreme enthusiasm for Rousseau, Napoleon had some dispute with his uncle, the Archdeacon Lucien, about the numerous herds of goats on Corsica : Napoleon claimed they damaged the trees. He was accused by his uncle, surprisingly, of being an "innovator", an agronome too imbued with "philosophical ideas". We have no evidence that Napoleon read any of the major works of agronomic theory, such as *La Nouvelle Maison Rustique* or the writings of Duhamel du Monceau – although in 1788 he did read some sections from the Abbé Raynal's *Philosophical History of Commerce in the two Indies* – so that perhaps he was considered to have gleaned his innovatory, agronomic notions from a less direct source : certainly *La Nouvelle Héloïse* often reads like a series of articles from the *Journal Oeconomique,* particularly in the sections on landlord/peasant relations, on domestic economy, and on the running of the vines at Clarens.

Whatever the polemical impact of the work on Napoleon he often modelled his letters – for example in the period 1795-7 – on *La Nouvelle Héloïse.* His letter to Josephine, written "le 29 Messidor, 9 heures du soir", which begins "I have received your letter, my adorable friend, it fills my heart with joy" is pure Rousseau. In ensuing years, his letters to Josephine were less ebullient, but there are still parallels : by contrast, Napoleon's letters to his brothers and proclamations to the army, dating from the same period, are more terse and staccato in style. In 1798, when he was sailing to Egypt, and still entertained hopes that an *Ossian* would accompany him to sing his praises, and a *Rousseau* to write simple, manageable tunes which would stay in the mind (on the pattern of *Le Devin du Village*), General Bonaparte still kept the work as his constant companion, for light reading.

Napoleon's relationship with *La Nouvelle Héloïse* is in many ways symbolic of his changing attitude to literature, and even of the development of his own talent as a writer. From early garrison days when he avidly read *Du Contrat Social* containing its famous prophecy about Corsica, through the interminably long evenings on board the flagship *Orient* sailing for Egypt, where the romantic young General hoped spectacularly to make his reputation, to the final weeks of exile, where Napoleon had nothing better to occupy his time, than to scribble random suggestions and caustic comments in the margin of a novel which could move him no more, we can see Napoleon's views on the *utility* of literature becoming more apparent.

Arnault writes that Napoleon started organising literary discussions at his house in the rue Chantereine, just before he embarked for Egypt. This may have been part of his drive to recruit well-known figures from the literary and musical worlds, to travel with him on the expedition. It was during these meetings that Napoleon's utilitarian views of literature were first offered in public.

I noticed, in the opinions of the master of the house on various works, his tendency to connect everything to his dominant interest at the time. He could never leave this out of account, and consider the compositions with reference to the goal that the author had in mind. Artistic productions, like scientific discoveries, were not entirely pleasing to him, except insofar as they had some useful application to his present needs. Once, I had proof of this on the occasion of one of my works. I had just read my *Venetians* at the Théâtre Français. When he was told of this, the General wanted to hear the work one day, after dinner – he wanted this as he wanted everything, that is to say without allowing the slightest delay, this evening, this very instant . . .

The play had a profound impression on all those present – even on the General himself. But after praising the care I had taken over local colour in my play, and the way in which I had remained faithful to the characteristic features of Venetian politics and mores . . .

"However" he said to me, "I have one criticism of your first act."

"What criticism, General?"

"It is that you do not depict the Venetian Senate in sufficiently odious colours."

"But I have not concealed the harshness of her institutions."

"You justify that harshness by the goal that the Senate has set itself – the support of independence."

"True, but such was the spirit that reigned in the Venetian Senate for six hundred years, the spirit which created the Council of Ten, and the Council of the Three . . . those aristocrats feared more than anything, that someone from among them would establish himself in power. They submitted to the tyranny of the law in order to escape the despotism of one of their fellows; they sacrificed their liberty – even their security – to their independence."

"But this advantage" he continued briskly, "can excuse the Venetian government of many things. So that perhaps we did wrong in taking advantage of her institutions to destroy the government."

This phrase, which revealed his whole train of thought to me, also revealed the tendency of his mind; a tendency which has manifested itself so openly since.

A Checklist of the Writings of Napoleon
1785-1796

(* = included in this volume)

DATE		PLACE	TITLE
1785		Paris	* Discourse on luxury in military schools.
1786		Valence	* Fable: The Hare, The Hound and the Huntsman.
	26 April		Reflections on Corsica.
	3 May		* Entry in Private Journal: On Suicide.
	9 May		Refutation of the *Defence of Christianity* by A-J Roustan (a reply to Ch. VIII, Bk. IV of Rousseau's *Du Contrat Social*).
1787	22 November	Paris	* Entry in Private Journal: A Meeting at the Palais Royal.
	27 November	Paris	Fragment on the misfortunes of Corsica.
	November-December	Paris	* A Parallel between Love of Glory and Love of Country. Letter of King Theodore to Walpole.
1788			Projected Constitution for 'La Calotte' (a Junior Officers' club in the regiment La Fère).
			Report on various artillery tests of August 1788.
	23 October	Auxonne	* Dissertation on Royal Authority.
1789	January	Auxonne	First note-book on the history of artillery.
	February		Outline of a history of artillery.
	30 March		Memorandum on the positioning of cannon for releasing explosive shells.
1788	October		Letter to General DuTeil.

Notes on political theory, natural history and political history, here listed in the order that Napoleon read the texts.

DATE		PLACE	TITLE
1789	August		Notes on Plato's 'Republic' (probably from Grou's French translation 1762). Some ideas on the government of ancient people. (Extracts from Rollin's *Ancient History* and other works on Persia, Greece and Sparta.
			Observations on the government of ancient Egypt, the dimensions of the Pyramids and the governments of Carthage, Assyria and Persia.
			Extracts from the *Philosophical history of Commerce in the two Indies* by the Abbé Raynal.
1788	November	Auxonne	* Notes on John Barrow's *History of England from earliest times to the peace of 1763*. (The French edition that Napoleon read stops in 1689, but still fills ten volumes.)
1789	January		* The Earl of Essex, an English Tale.
1788	December		Notes from the History of King Frederic II (mainly on the Seven Years War).
			Various notes taken from the memoirs of the Abbé Terray, controller general, on his life and the administration of finances.
			More notes from Terray—specifically on Commerce in the Indies.
			Notes on J. G. Lavater's *Art of Judging Character from Men's faces*.
1789	January		Notes taken from the Memoirs of Baron de Tott, on the Turks and the Tartars.
			On *Lettres de Cachets* by the Count de Mirabeau.
1789	February		Notes taken from *The English Spy, or secret correspondence between Lord All'Eye and Lord All'Ear*.
1789	March	Auxonne	Extracts, with assorted comments, from Buffon's *Natural History*, and from Bernardin de St. Pierre's *Studies of Nature* (on the theory of tides).
			Notes on the customs of different peoples, subdivided into sections on children, expectation of life, virginity and sterility.

DATE	PLACE	TITLE
		Tables of statistics on expectation of life, with data from twelve country parishes and three Paris parishes, from the findings of M. du Pré de St. Maur (from Buffon).
1789 March/April	Seurre	* Various notes taken from the *History of the Arab peoples under the government of the Caliphs* by the Abbé Marigny.
		* The Mask of the Prophet—an Arabian Tale.
1789 May	Seurre/ Auxonne	Extracts from the *Government of Venice* (with political and historical notes) by Amelot de la Houssaie.
1789 9 May	Auxonne	Notes on M. Necker's report of the 5th May 1789 at the opening of the Estates General.
8-11 June	Auxonne	Notes and extracts from the Gazettes, and other public papers (including an account of the Debate on Slavery in the House of Commons, with a summary of Wilberforce's propositions).
August	Auxonne	Notes from *Observations on the History of France* by the Abbé de Mably. Various extracts and notes from *Modern Geography* by the Abbé de Lacroix.
		Letters to M. Necker on Corsica (no longer extant).
		* New Corsica, a Corsican Tale.
31 October	Ajaccio	Address to the National Assembly on the manifesto of the Commission of the twelve.
1789-90		Letters to M. l'Abbé Raynal on Corsica. (A detailed history of the island, leading up to the third letter which contains an extended lament on the Corsican situation.)
1790 June	Ajaccio	
		Proclamation of the municipal body of the town of Ajaccio—after the day of 25 June 1790 (with a justificatory memoir).
August	Bastia	Chronological notes on the Old Testament.

DATE	PLACE	TITLE
1791	23 January	Corsica	Letter to M. Matteo Buttafuoco, deputy from Corsica at the National Assembly.
1791	8 February	St. Vallier	Entry in Private Journal: on attitudes to love and friendship, and how they develop.
April/June	Auxonne	Notes on the *History of the Sorbonne* by the Abbé Duvernet: topics include Papal authority, and the Gallican/ Ultramontane controversy.
10 April 1 May 5 May 1 August	Auxonne	Various jottings, including a list of polysyllabic words for possible inclusion in the *Discours de Lyon*.
20 and 24 April	Auxonne	Notes on William Coxe's *Travels in Switzerland*.
11 May	Auxonne	Notes on Duclos' *Secret Memoirs of the reigns of Louis XIV and XV*.
12 May	Auxonne	Notes on the *Esprit de Gerson* by Eustache le Noble (an account of the major differences between the doctirnes of the French church and those of Bellarmine and the ultramontanes). These notes contain a résumé of Napoleon's thoughts on Gallicanism.
19 May	Auxonne	Extracts from *A critical history of the nobility from the beginnings of monarchy to the present day* by M. Dulaure.
22 May	Auxonne	Notes on Voltaire's *Essay on Manners*.
24 June	Valence	Extracts from Machiavelli's *History of Florence* (from the 1789 translation into French).
June or July		* Republic or Monarchy. * Dialogue on Love. Notes on Rousseau's *Discourse on the Origin of Inequality among men* and an essay on the state of nature.
August	Valence	Random jottings for the *Discours de Lyon*.
August	Partly written in Valence	* Discourse on the question set by the Academy of Lyon: what sentiments and what truths should be inculcated in men for their happiness?

DATE		PLACE	TITLE
1789	Between August and July (possibly)		* Clisson and Eugénie.
1792	Between May and September	Paris	* A Madrigal dedicated to Madame Saint-Huberty, after her triumph in Piccini's opera *Dido*.
	March or April	Ajaccio	Rules for keeping order in the battalion of National Guards.
	April	Ajaccio	Report to justify the battalion of volunteers for the disturbances of the month of April.
1793	2 March		Declaration of the volunteers on the subject of the decision to abandon the counter-attack on Sardinia.
	February to April	Ajaccio	Report on the necessity of gaining control of the Islands of Maddalena (Caprera, Saint Etienne and Maddalena).
	1 March	Bonifacio	Project for another attack on the Island and town of Maddalena.
		Ajaccio	Various addresses to the Society of friends of the People in Ajaccio.
		Ajaccio	Project for the defence of the gulf of Saint-Florent.
			Project for the defence of the gulf of Ajaccio.
	Between 1 April and 1 June	Ajaccio	Addresses of the Society of friends of the People to the Convention and to the municipality of Ajaccio (on the subject of the Convention's decree against Paoli).
		Ajaccio	Petition to the citizens of the town of Ajaccio (encouraging them to take the oath of allegiance and union to the French Republic).
	1 June		Memoir on the political and military position of the Department of Corsica.
1793	July (completed 29 July)	Written in Avignon or possibly Nice Published in Avignon	* Supper in Beaucaire, or a Discussion between a Soldier of Carteaux' army, a Marseillais, a man from Nîmes and a manufacturer from Montpellier, on the events which have occurred in the former country on the arrival of the men from Marseilles.

A Checklist   171

DATE		PLACE	TITLE
1795	August- September (possibly)	Paris	* Clisson and Eugenie.
1796		Near Modena	Inscription for a sun-dial, written on a farm where Napoleon had been treated hospitably, near the Via Emilia (between Reggio and Modena). The inscription reads: 'L'ombre passe et repasse, Et sans repasser l'homme passe.'

This checklist has been compiled from Martel, Masson and Biagi, Chuquet, Healey, Tomiche-Dagher and my own research discoveries.

Select Bibliography

I. THE WRITINGS OF NAPOLEON

Martel, T., ed. *Oeuvres Littéraires de Napoléon Bonaparte.* Paris, 1888. ('The Hare, The Hound and the Huntsman'. The Madrigal. Discourse on Luxury in Military Schools.)

Masson, F., and G. Biagi, eds. Napoléon Inconnu: Papiers Inédits (1786-93). Paris, 1895. (Essays, Notes and Short Stories.)

Cahuet, Albéric, ed. Article in 'L'Illustration' of Saturday 17 January, 1920 (number 4011). (Clisson and Eugénie.)

Askenazy, S., ed. Manuscrits de Napoléon (1793-5) en Pologne. Warsaw, 1929. (another transcription of Clisson and Eugénie, with variants.)

Samuel, Nigel, M.S. The middle section of Clisson and Eugénie.

Bonaparte, Napoleon. Le Souper de Beaucaire. Avignon, 1793.

Bonaparte, Napoleon. Memoirs (edited by Somerset de Chair). London, 1948.

Bonaparte, Napoleon. Correspondance générale. Publiée par ordre de L'Empereur Napoléon III.) Paris, 1858-70.

Chuquet, A., ed. Inédits Napoleoniéns. Paris, 1913-16. (Mainly for biographical material).

Reverdin, O. Article in Annales de la Société Jean-Jacques Rousseau, vol. XXX. Geneva, 1943-5. (Napoleon's criticisms of 'La Nouvelle Héloïse').

Catalogue des ouvrages de Napoléon Ier et de Napoléon III conservés au Departement des Imprimés. Paris, 1933. (A bibliography from La Bibliothèque Nationale.)

II. MEMOIRS AND EYE-WITNESS ACCOUNTS OF NAPOLEON'S LIFE

Arnault, A-V. Souvenirs d'un Sexagénaire. Paris, 1833.

Bertrand, H. G. Cahiers de Sainte-Hélène: Journal 1816-21. (Manuscrit dechiffré et annoté par P. Fleuriot de Langle). Paris, 1959.

Boswell, J. On the Grand Tour: Italy, Corsica and France 1765-6. (Yale edition). London, 1955. The Journal of a tour to Corsica, and Memoirs of Pascal Paoli, London, 1951.

Bourrienne, de, L-A. F. Private Memoirs of Napoleon Bonaparte. London, 1830.

Cases, E. de Las, Journal of the Private Life and Conversations of the Emperor Napoleon at Saint Helena, London, 1823.

Domairon, L. Principes généraux des Belles-Lettres. Paris, 1784-5.

Gourgaud, G. The Saint Helena Journal 1815-18. London, 1932.

Méneval, C. F., de. Mémoires pour servir à L'Histoire de Napoléon Ier depuis 1802 jusqu'à 1815. Paris, 1894.

Rémusat, C. E. J., de. Memoirs 1802-8. Published by P. de Rémusat. London, 1880.

Roederer, P-L. Bonaparte me disait . . . (Extracts from Roederer's Journal). Paris, 1942.

III. SECONDARY SOURCES

(a) *General*

Cronin, V. Napoleon. London, 1971.

Follain, J. Napoléon. Paris, 1967.

Iung, T. Bonaparte et son temps 1769-99, d'après les documents inédits. 1880-1.

Lefebvre, G. Napoléon (Peuples et Civilisations, 14) Paris, 1935.

Markham, F. Napoleon and the Awakening of Europe. London, 1954.

Napoleon: A Biography. London, 1963.

Thompson, G. M. Napoleon Bonaparte: His rise and fall. Oxford, 1952.

Wilkinson, H. S. The rise of General Bonaparte. Oxford, 1930.

(b) *Napoleon's Early Life and Schooldays.*

Bartel, P. La jeunesse inédite de Napoléon. Paris, 1954.

Chuquet, A. La jeunesse de Napoléon. Paris, 1897-9.

Masson, F. Napoléon dans sa jeunesse. Paris, 1907.

Parker, H. T. Article in French Historical Studies, Spring, 1971.

(c) *Napoleon and Literature.*

Healey, F. G. The Literary Culture of Napoleon. Geneva, 1959.

Rousseau et Napoléon. Geneva, 1957.

Herold, J. C. The Mind of Napoleon, 1955.

Mouravit, G. Napoléon Bibliophile. Paris, 1905.

Holland Rose, J. The Personality of Napoleon. London, 1912.

Tomiche-Dagher, N. Napoléon Ecrivain. Paris 1952.